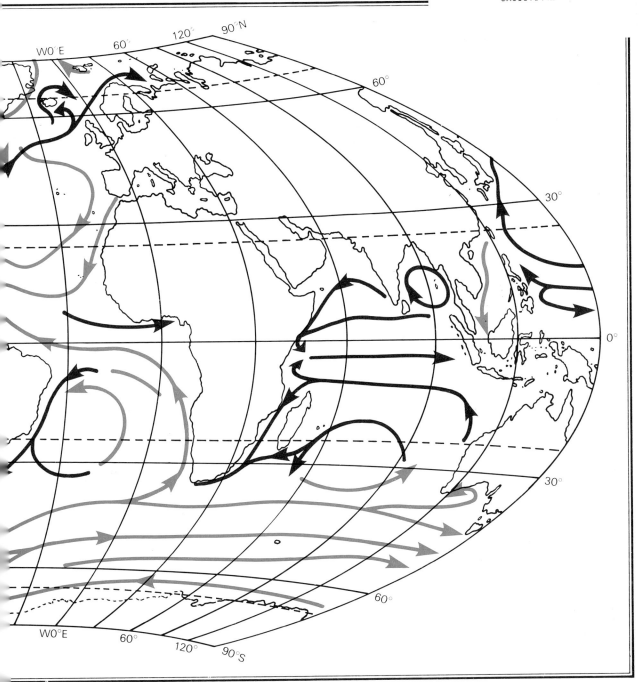

Historical Instruments in
OCEANOGRAPHY

Background to the
Oceanography
Collection at the
Science Museum

Anita McConnell

LONDON   HER MAJESTY'S STATIONERY OFFICE

© *Crown copyright 1981*
First published 1981

Cover: Tony Stone Photolibrary – London

Designed by HMSO Graphic Design

HER MAJESTY'S STATIONERY OFFICE
Government Bookshops

49 High Holborn, London WC1V 6HB
13a Castle Street, Edinburgh EH2 3AR
41 The Hayes, Cardiff CF1 1JW
Brazennose Street, Manchester M60 8AS
Southey House, Wine Street, Bristol BS1 2BQ
258 Broad Street, Birmingham B1 2HE
80 Chichester Street, Belfast BT1 4JY
Government publications are also available
through booksellers

A large range of Museum publications
is displayed and sold at
The Science Museum, London SW7 2DD

ISBN 0 11 290324 X

Typeset by Input Typesetting Ltd
Printed in England for
Her Majesty's Stationery Office
by Shenval '80', Harlow.
Dd 696352 C50 8/81

Contents

The aim of this handbook is to set the Science Museum Oceanography Collection against its historical background. For more detailed histories of Oceanography readers are referred to the 'Further Reading' list at the end of this handbook.

The Science Museum has other Collections related to the marine sciences which do not form part of the Oceanography Collection and are thus not described in this handbook. They are:

Tidal measurement, analysis and prediction.
Navigation and hydrographic surveying.
Diving and submersible craft.
Acoustics, including underwater acoustics and sonar.

The Geological Museum has displays showing underwater geology, and the Natural History Museum deals with all aspects of marine biology and zoology.

ACKNOWLEDGEMENT

Illustrations in this book have been prepared in the Science Museum's Photostudio and Drawing Office, with the exception of Figure 57, which is reproduced by kind permission of Sir Alister Hardy.

1 GENERAL INTRODUCTION
Seas and Oceans

Oceans cover 70 per cent of the planet on which we live. We can speak of a World Ocean, in the sense that it is possible to sail continuously around the world. More commonly we define three major oceans; the Pacific, Atlantic and Indian Oceans, which are largely separated by continents, so that circulation of their waters is restricted. Oceanographers can use the conventional geographic divisions of three major and many minor oceans and seas because the nature of the water differs within each of these areas.

Oceanography is the study of the oceans; their form, the nature of seawater and of the ocean floor, together with their varied forms of plant and animal life. Oceanic processes are so varied that the science is usually subdivided: physical oceanography deals with waves, currents and all movement of the water; chemical oceanography concerns the chemical constituents and reactions occurring within and between seawater and sea floor sediments; geological oceanography is concerned with structure and processes in the sea bed and the underlying rocks; biological oceanography, or marine biology, deals with all forms of life within the sea.

Before describing the history of exploration in the oceans, it is useful to summarise briefly what is known today about these great volumes of water which occupy the major proportion of the earth's surface.

The principal topographic divisions of the oceans are: the *continental margins* (comprising *shelves, slopes* and *rises*); the *abyssal plains*; and the *oceanic ridges*. Continental margins are submerged extensions of the land masses. The extent of these margins has varied throughout geological history. We know this because rocks containing marine fossils occur over three-quarters of the present land surface. The continental shelves extend on average 50 km from the present shoreline, though this distance is very variable. They are covered by sediments derived largely from nearby land, together with detritus from marine organisms. The shelf terminates abruptly at the continental slope, which drops fairly steeply to considerable depths, of the order of 2000 to 3000 metres. From here the continental rise levels out gently, meeting the abyssal plains at 4000 to 5000 metres depth. These plains make up over one third of the area of the Atlantic and Indian Ocean basins and three-quarters of the Pacific basin. Blanketed by fine clays, they are featureless apart from volcanic islands and submerged *seamounts* which often occur in clusters connected on the sea floor by the accumulations from volcanic activity and erosion. The ocean ridge systems form a series of interconnected ranges, rising two to four kilometres above the ocean floor. They represent the *constructive margins* of the tectonic plates making up the earth's crust. Along these ridges material from deep within the earth is rising to the surface and spreading out to create new areas of ocean floor. This generation of new floor is counterbalanced elsewhere by movement down into the mantle at *destructive plate-margins*. The steep-sided trenches, where sea floor is being pulled down, are the deepest parts of the ocean. The distance from the sea surface to the trench floor may be over 10 000 metres. Topographical range within the oceans is therefore much greater than on land, where the highest peak, Mount Everest, rises 8884 metres above sea level.

It is thought that seawater, with its characteristic ratio of dissolved salts, has been accumulating throughout geological time. New water accompanies basaltic rocks pushed up at ocean ridges, and is also derived from volcanoes.

The *salinity* of seawater is measured as the total number of grams of dissolved salt in one kilogram of seawater. In the open sea salinity ranges from 33‰ (parts per thousand) to 38‰.

The major constituents, which are mostly present in ionic form, are sodium, potassium, calcium and magnesium. In fact, almost all elements are present, in very small amounts, in sea water. There are also variable quantities of nutrients such as nitrogen compounds, phosphate, silicate and oxygen (gas). These, together with water and bicarbonates, make up compounds essential to all plant and animal life.

We can think of the oceans as a gigantic heat pump transferring heat from the equator to the poles. Surface water flow is guided by the winds and by forces due to the earth's rotation and the shape of the ocean basins. In the middle latitude of both hemispheres prevailing westerly winds set up an eastwards drift. In the southern hemisphere this drift in not interrupted by land masses and so circulates around the Antarctic continent as a continuous *west-wind drift*. In the northern hemisphere the drift is obstructed by continents, which deflect it both north and south. In the North Atlantic, a vast clockwise eddy, of which the Gulf Stream is an important part, is thus established. The South Atlantic, and the other oceans have similar eddies or *gyres* (Figure 1, inside cover).

When the surface currents reach polar latitudes they are chilled, and their salinity is increased by the formation of ice floes from which most of the salt is excluded. The water thus becomes very dense, and sinks to the bottom, returning equatorwards through the deeper parts of the ocean.

The global circulation results in a temperature profile through the water with three main features: a surface or *mixed layer*, which may be a few tens or hundreds of metres thick, reflecting the average air temperatures in that latitude; below this is an intermediate *thermocline* region, where there is a fairly abrupt change in temperature with depth to that of; a *deep bottom layer*, of polar origin, with temperatures a few degrees above the freezing point of seawater (which is around $-2°C$, depending on salinity). Deep bottom water is normally found at depths below one or two kilometres. In polar seas therefore, the surface water is often colder than that at depth, while the converse is true for temperate and tropical seas.

Within the sea, pressure increases by one atmosphere every ten metres. 5000 metres down, on the abyssal plains, it is 500 times greater than at the surface. In the deepest trenches, 10 kilometres down, the pressure is over 100 kilogrammes per square millimetre.

Plant life flourishes where sunlight penetrates the water, forming the primary stage in the marine food chain. As on land, fertile regions and deserts exist, depending on the presence or absence of nutrients. Generally speaking, shallow seas are rich feeding grounds, so too are those zones where water wells up from depth, carrying nutrients with it. Elsewhere life may be more sparse.

Much of the ocean's volume is pitch dark, cold, and under great pressure. Nevertheless, life has adapted to this environment and marine organisms are to be found in every region, both in the water and at the sea floor (Figure 2).

FIGURE 2 A variety of instruments serve to investigate the physics and chemistry of the sea

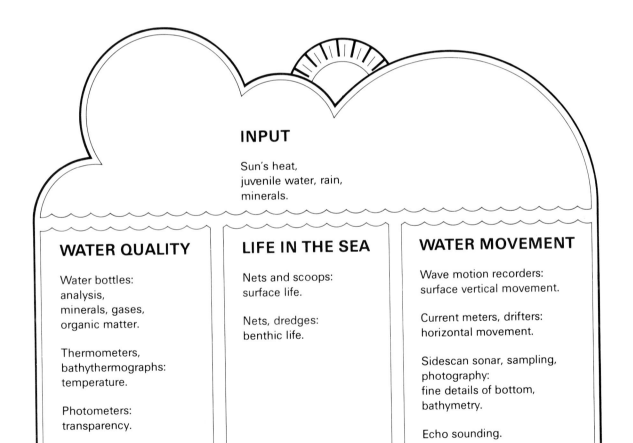

INPUT

Sun's heat,
juvenile water, rain,
minerals.

WATER QUALITY

Water bottles:
analysis,
minerals, gases,
organic matter.

Thermometers,
bathythermographs:
temperature.

Photometers:
transparency.

LIFE IN THE SEA

Nets and scoops:
surface life.

Nets, dredges:
benthic life.

WATER MOVEMENT

Wave motion recorders:
surface vertical movement.

Current meters, drifters:
horizontal movement.

Sidescan sonar, sampling,
photography:
fine details of bottom,
bathymetry.

Echo sounding.

FIGURE 3 Replicas of Hooke's
waywiser sounder (right)
thermoscope (centre) and water
sampler (left)

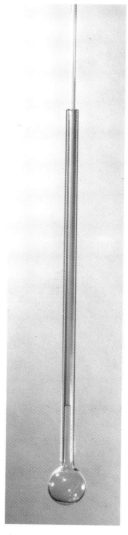
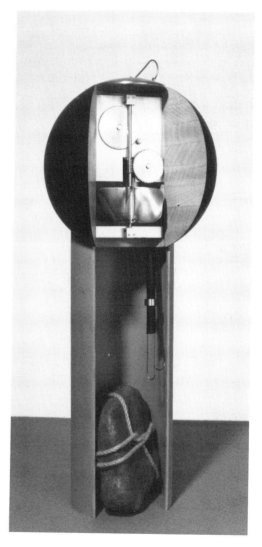

Researches stimulated by the Scientific Revolution, 1650–1850

From the earliest times men have sailed across the world ocean, taking their families and livestock to colonise even those islands most remote from land. Sailors, explorers and fishermen have observed conditions at the sea surface and at its tidal margins. Such knowledge was often kept a closely guarded secret for commercial reasons. Knowing the depth of shallow seas, and the nature of the bottom, enabled navigators to avoid running aground and to find good anchorages and fishing grounds. Of the depths beyond, and of the nature of the deep water, its submarine temperatures and currents, they could only speculate. Their charts might show off-shore soundings but the spaces of open sea bear only a compass rose or representations of those creatures thought to inhabit the unfathomable depths.

To a ship's captain, the sea is primarily a *surface*. His marine skills are therefore those of navigation and its sister arts: astronomy and hydrography. When, during the scientific revolution of the 17th century, interest arose concerning marine science, the apparatus available for investigating conditions at sea was that used by navigators and marine surveyors, namely, the sounding lead and the ship's log; and that used by chemists in their laboratories ashore: the thermometer and hydrometer. It was soon realised that the sounding lead and thermometer would not work satisfactorily in deep water, for reasons which will be shown, but which were not then understood. There was no way of bringing up samples of water from below the surface in order to measure its salinity by means of the hydrometer, nor of measuring sub-surface currents.

In Britain the Royal Society encouraged marine science, and many accounts of such studies appeared in the Society's *Philosophical Transactions*, first published in 1665. Robert Hooke (1635–1703) came to the Royal Society as Curator of Experiments in 1662, and while there devised many ingenious contrivances for investigating the sea. Some of his designs were constructed, but were tested only in the calm waters of the river where he demonstrated them to members of the society. Nevertheless he had some successes, and his water-sampler served as a prototype which was later modified into more practical forms.

The illustrations show (Figure 3) Hooke's water sampler, thermoscope and sounder, reconstructed by the Science Museum. The sampler, or waterbottle, was made of wood. Lowered on a line, the flow of water kept the end-valves open until the instrument was hauled up, bringing with it a sample from the depth reached. In practice, wood is totally unsuited to such apparatus; at quite small depths it becomes waterlogged, and the simple end-valves shown would not keep the sample uncontaminated on its passage to the surface.

The thermoscope had a globe filled with spirits of wine. The inner glass tube had a valve at its bottom end, though this is not shown on Hooke's drawing or on our reconstruction. On being lowered into cold water the spirits of wine contracted, drawing down the inner tube. When the thermoscope was hauled in, the expanding spirit passed through the valve up into the inner tube. The length between the inner and outer tubes was therefore a measure of the difference in temperature at the surface and at the depth to which the instrument had been lowered. Such an instrument would be affected far more by pressure than by temperature.

The sounder shown here worked on the same principal as a waywiser or ship's log. A vane was turned by the flow of water as the instrument sank, and this vane moved a series of toothed wheels and a pointer which indicated the distance travelled. The instrument was thrown overboard with a weight fastened to a spring clip below the wooden sphere. In theory, the sounder operated on the way down; the spring clip detached the weight on striking bottom, and the float brought the assembly to the surface where it could be recovered and the counter read. In practice, the sounder might have been carried some distance from the ship by currents, and in any case, except in very calm water, the float was not easily seen when it reappeared at the surface.

Hooke incorporated both the sounder and sampler principles shown in these instruments to describe a composite apparatus (Figure 4) which measured the distance travelled both up and down through the water, as well as recovering two water samples, one of these being secured on the way up by means of a trigger operated by the sounder cogs. As illustrated here this apparatus is mechanically impractical. Like most other non-seafaring men of his day, Hooke never realised that wood becomes waterlogged at depth and therefore no instruments employing wood in their construction could be used for oceanography.

A matter which concerned the British Navy during the 17th and later centuries was the flow of currents through the Straits of Gibraltar. A surface current flowed into the Mediterranean, and it was thought that a counter-current might flow out beneath the surface, though both currents apparently varied in position and strength from one season to another. A submarine current will affect the way of a ship towing fishing nets or a sea-anchor, and a modification of this principal was suggested by Richard Bolland, a hydrographical surveyor making a survey of the Straits during the 1660s. He suggested two methods of detecting the submarine current but died before carrying out the work.

In 1679 the Italian scientist Count Luigi-Ferdinando di Marsigli (1658–1730), using simply a weighted line carrying white-painted cork discs, detected just such a system of currents and submarine counter-currents flowing through the Bosphorus (Figure 5). Marsigli also measured the density of water from the two currents and was able to explain that lighter fresher water flowed out from the Black Sea over the saltier bottom counter-current flowing in from

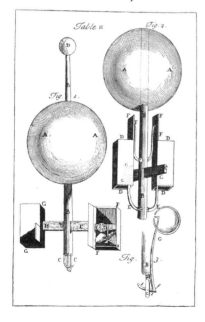

FIGURE 4 Hooke's multiple sounder and water sampler

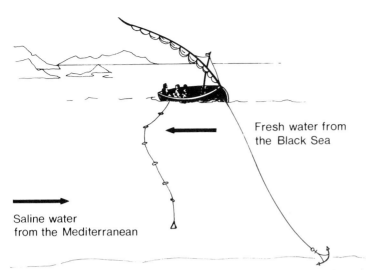

Fresh water from
the Black Sea

Saline water
from the Mediterranean

the Mediterranean. He carried out many other successful observations on the waters of the western Mediterranean, including their temperatures, salinities and currents. He also studied the nature of the sea bed and its plant and animal life. The book in which he described his methods and his findings was published in Amsterdam in 1725.*

Another regional study of the Mediterranean, carried out mostly off the coast of Algeria, was that of Georges Aimé (1810–1846), member of a commission charged with the exploration of Algeria. Aimé was intrigued by the movements of the sea. He had few resources available to him; a small boat and occasional helpers. Despite this, by devising a series of instruments, he was able to carry out and write up important observations on the water movements due to waves, tides and sub-surface current. In addition, he constructed a thermometer and a sounder both of which operated by messenger release (Figure 6).

The principal of messenger release is as follows: an iron or lead ring is secured round the line carrying apparatus. When it is desired to operate the apparatus, the ring, or messenger, is released from the ship and slides down the line to strike a trigger mechanism. By this means an instrument may be caused to operate at any depth within the water. Messenger release is commonly used at the present time for triggering waterbottle and thermometer apparatus.

Aimé's thermometer was of the overflow type. The messenger caused it to detach from its holder and to reverse as the apparatus was hauled in. The level of mercury corresponding to the temperature at the depth of reversal was trapped by this action, and could therefore be read off when the instrument was recovered on board.

Aimé's instruments were technically advanced compared to many others in use elsewhere at this period. His death at the age of 36 (he fell from his horse whilst on a geological expedition in Algeria) terminated a promising career and his work was rather overlooked, especially in Britain. Some of his original instruments are preserved in the Oceanographical Museum, Monaco.

* L-F de Marsigli: *Histoire Physique de la Mer*. Amsterdam 1725.

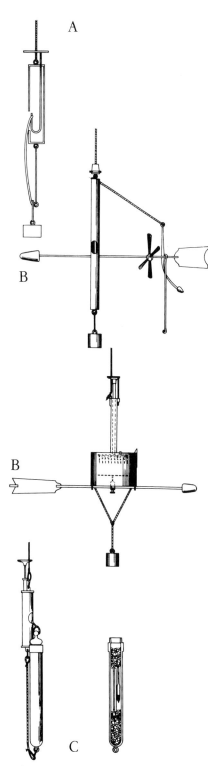

A

B

B

C

FIGURE 6 Aimé's messenger-operated instruments: sounder (a) current meters (b) and thermometer (c)

The men whose work has been described above all carried out their researches privately. (Hooke and Aimé, though technically in employment, were able to devote only a limited amount of their time to marine sciences.) Their scope was therefore limited, both in the area that they could cover and in the depths at which they could work. In the days before the invention of the steam-powered donkey engine the physical effort of hauling in more than a few fathoms of rope required the labour of many men around a capstan. This in itself necessitated the use of a large vessel, rather than a small boat, as did any voyage lasting more than a few hours. The hire of such a ship and crew represented considerable expense, while scientific research, then as now, was not expected to yield immediate financial returns.

Wider-ranging comprehensive investigations could only be carried out with government backing. Institutions such as the Royal Society often suggested a programme of research which was then undertaken by Royal Navy vessels and crews. The situation was much the same in France, and during the latter part of the 18th century several expeditions having a deliberate scientific mission in addition to the geographical exploration of the seas were sent out from Britain and from France.

Investigations in Arctic and Antarctic waters, 1773–1850

During the course of the 18th century the Admiralty despatched several pairs of ships on voyages of exploration into distant waters (Figure 7). Frequently their crews had some specific scientific task to fulfil, designed to improve the art of navigation. Perhaps the most famous of these voyages is that of Captain James Cook who, in 1769, sailed into the Pacific for the purpose of observing the Transit of Venus from the island of Tahiti.*

During the same period the Royal Society persuaded Lord Sandwich (First Lord of the Admiralty) to seek Royal Sanction for a naval expedition to search for an Arctic route through to the Pacific Ocean. The request was granted, and two small strong vessels, of the type known as 'bombs', were prepared for the voyage. HMS *Racehorse*, with a crew of 90 men, was commanded by Captain Constantine Phipps (later Lord Mulgrave). Accompanied by the smaller HMS *Carcass* she set sail in June 1773. The scientific work undertaken during the cruise was intended to resolve certain prob-

---

* Knowing the diameter of the earth, if the time that the planet Venus passed across the sun's disc could be observed at two widely-separated places then the sun's diameter and its distance from the earth could be calculated.

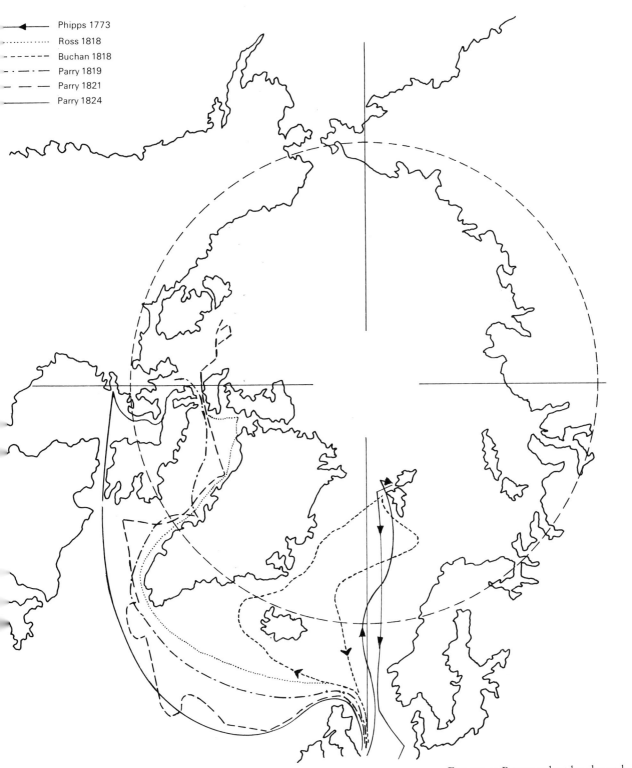

Phipps 1773
Ross 1818
Buchan 1818
Parry 1819
Parry 1821
Parry 1824

FIGURE 7 Routes taken by the early
Arctic expeditions

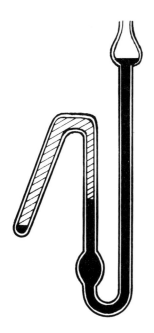

FIGURE 8 Cavendish's deep sea minimum thermometer

lems of navigation in high latitudes where the proximity of the earth's Magnetic Pole made compass readings unreliable.

Phipps took the opportunity during calm weather to make observations of the depth and temperature of the sea, and to measure current flow. He was equipped with a minimum thermometer of the overflow type, proposed by Lord Cavendish in 1757 as a deep sea thermometer, and this was sent down on his sounding line on several occasions (Figure 8).

Aware of the possible effect of pressure on his thermometer, Phipps tried an alternative method of measuring the water temperature. With the help of the ship's surgeon, Dr Irving, he insulated a bottle by wrapping it in a series of wool, oilskin, leather and tarred canvas covers, hoping by this means to bring a sample of water to the surface without its temperature being changed on the way up. It might then be measured on deck, where the thermometer would give a reading which was not affected by pressure. The observations which he obtained by the two different methods did not coincide. Phipps had no means of telling which was correct; with hindsight we now know that his thermometer was unreliable at depth; that in the Arctic Ocean the deepest water is not always the coldest; and that Irving's waterbottle was unlikely to have recovered water from precisely the depth intended (Figure 9).

Phipps' cruise lasted only a few weeks. He was unable to penetrate the ice pack between East Greenland and Spitzbergen, and in August the onset of bad weather forced him to turn southwards. He arrived home in September, and in the following year published an account of his voyage which included descriptions and tabulated results of all his scientific work.*

FIGURE 9 Suggested form of Irving's waterbottle

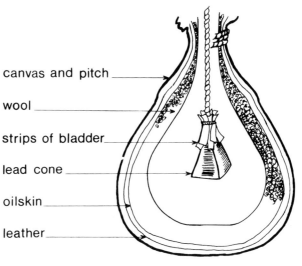

canvas and pitch
wool
strips of bladder
lead cone
oilskin
leather

* C. J. Phipps. A voyage towards the North Pole. London 1774.

Phipps' expedition had sailed during an era when the ice pack extended relatively far south. In the early years of the 19th century unusually large quantities of ice broke away from the pack and floated into the Atlantic. By 1817 whaling vessels reported that the east coast of Greenland, inaccessible for some four hundred years, was clear as far as 80°N, and the sea between this coast and the island of Spitzbergen free of ice. The obstacle that had barred Phipps from entering the Arctic Ocean having apparently vanished, the Admiralty decided that the time had come to search again for a way through to Bering's Straits and the Pacific Ocean.

In 1818 the Admiralty despatched two expeditions towards the Arctic. Under Captain John Ross HMS *Isabella* and HMS *Alexander* (Lt W. E. Parry) were ordered to sail west of Greenland, through Davis Strait, and look for an open seaway that would allow them to pass along the northern edge of the American continent. The other ships, HMS *Dorothea*, under Captain David Buchan and HMS *Trent* (Lt J. Franklin), were to keep east of Greenland and attempt the direct trans-polar route to the Pacific Ocean.

All four vessels were fitted out to make them as strong and as well-supplied as possible for they might be away for several years. A number of new instruments were sent, and it was hoped that even if the main object of the voyage were not achieved, a worthwhile advancement of science would be gained.

In addition to the magnetical, meteorological and gravity observations, the instructions that Ross was given included some marine research. He was enjoined 'also endeavour to ascertain the set and direction of the currents, depth of the sea and nature of the bottom, and take up several samples of seawater'. By testing the water in various inlets it was hoped to distinguish between landlocked bays and straits leading to open ocean. The water in a bay, fed by melting ice, would be less salt than the main body of the ocean, whereas water in a strait would be of normal salinity and would probably have strong currents running through it. Ross's account of this expedition and its scientific work was published the following year.*

When John Ross sailed in 1818 he took with him the self-registering thermometer that had been invented by James Six in 1780. The thermometer consisted of a folded glass tube, alcohol filled the central reservoir and the upper portion of the left-hand limb, being separated by a mercury sector occupying the U-bend. In each outer limb light steel-in-glass indexes floated in the spirit. As the temperature changed, the mercury sector was propelled up one or other of the limbs. It pushed the indexes before it, leaving them behind to mark the extremes of temperature that had been reached.

Six originally designed this thermometer for measuring air temperatures and he supposed that alterations were necessary to allow it to work satisfactorily within the sea. He even constructed a version for deep-sea use, with thicker glass to resist pressure and indexes of a different type. But after his death it was found that his

FIGURE 10 Six's original thermometers: for use on land (left) and in the sea (right)

* J. Ross. A voyage of discovery in HMSS *Isabella* and *Alexander*. London 1819.

11

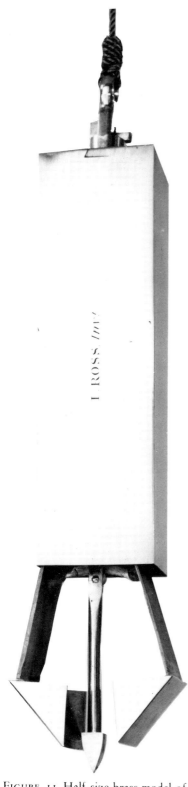

'air' thermometer worked adequately in the sea, providing that the end of its tube was sealed to keep the seawater out (Figure 10).

Six's thermometer was first used at sea on Krusenstern's voyage of circumnavigation during the years 1802 to 1806 in the Russian vessels *Neva* and *Nadeshda*. It was taken on the majority of expeditions, in the years that followed.

Some of the apparatus that was supplied to the expedition proved so unsatisfactory that Ross designed two new instruments himself during the course of the voyage. The ship's armourer constructed the deep-sea 'clamm' (Figure 11 shows a half-size model made from brass) which was a heavy iron grab intended to recover a large quantity of bottom sediment. Ross found that such a sample preserved the temperature of the sea bed, so that by thrusting a thermometer into the mass when it was brought up onto the deck he could discover the coldness of the bottom of the ocean basin. By this means, he found that mud from a depth of 420 fathoms in Melville Sound had a temperature of 29½°F, while his Six's thermometer, lowered at the same time to 210 fathoms, had a similar temperature. In one instance he claimed to have used the clamm to sound in 1000 fathoms. We now know that the area that he was in at the time is only 500 to 600 fathoms deep. Ross put out 1000 fathoms of line and was either not able to 'feel' bottom, or else had the line swept out of plumb by sub-surface currents. This illustrates the difficulties under which these early researches were made; there was no way that they could tell if their depth measurements were accurate, and without knowing the true depth, they could not tell what compensation for pressure was needed to obtain a true temperature reading from their thermometers.

One important result came from Ross's attempts at deep sounding: on several occasions he brought up bottom-dwelling creatures from depths greater than were thought habitable. For some reason, perhaps the general failure of the expedition (the ships returned without having located an entrance to the Northwest Passage) this great discovery was overlooked and for many years thereafter zoologists clung to the concept of an 'azoic' zone, probably below 300 fathoms, in which total darkness, cold, and great pressure made life insupportable.

Ross was issued with a waterbottle made to the design of Sir Humphry Davy, shortly before the voyage (Figure 12). The bottle was triggered to open at a preselected depth by an ingenious mechanism operated by pressure. Ross was not satisfied with the bottle, however, finding it unreliable in its operation. He therefore designed a container which he named a 'Hydrophorus'. From his illustration, it seems as complex as the Davy bottle and had it ever been tried would probably have been equally troublesome. At the time however, it was not realised that mechanical devices often jammed in deep water, as a result of the great pressures involved.

Meanwhile, Lieutenant Franklin, on board HMS *Trent*, had been issued with a waterbottle similar to that rejected by Phipps and Irving in 1773 – a cylindrical container whose lids closed on hauling

FIGURE 11 Half-size brass model of Ross's deep sea clamm

12

up. He also took with him the first bottle made by Alexander Marcet (1770–1822), a chemist interested in analysis of seawater from different parts of the oceans. Marcet knew that when the simple valved bottle was hauled in, it was impossible to keep a steady pull on the line against the motion of the waves and the pitching of the ship. He thought it probable that the valves would reopen and every sample would be contaminated by near-surface water. His improvement was to contrive a spring mechanism, whereby a heavy weight kept the valves open until, on striking bottom, the spring closed and held the valves secure whatever the subsequent movement of line and bottle (Figure 13).

Franklin found this bottle too light in construction for any but the shallowest waters, nor could it collect mid-water samples. Accordingly Marcet redesigned it, making a sturdy heavy apparatus with positive operation at any required depth (Figure 14).

The bottle had an opening top and bottom, closed by conical plugs joined by a central shaft. From the ship's deck a heavy weight was released down the line, and when it struck a lever on the bottle frame, the spring mechanism closed and locked the end-plugs. This type of bottle was employed on a number of naval expeditions, beginning with William Parry's Arctic voyage with *Hecla* and *Griper* in 1819–20.

In succeeding years many expeditions sailed from Britain into Arctic waters. Parry himself made three voyages. John Franklin failed to return from his third attempt to cross the Canadian Arctic shores, and his disappearance led to the despatch of various rescue parties. Most of the explorers were searching for a Northwest Passage, though it was by now obvious that if found it would offer no easy alternative to the Cape Horn route to the Pacific and indeed it might well be closed by ice for years at a time. John Ross sailed north again in 1829–33, accompanied by his nephew James Clark Ross, who finally established the location of the North Magnetic Pole. James Ross was himself chosen to lead the scientific expedition to the Antarctic, the aims being mainly in the field of terrestrial magnetism. However, as was now generally accepted practice, he was given instructions to carry out investigations into the temperature and depth of the sea, and the set of the currents. The difficulty of getting an accurate deep sea sounding was recognised and a suggestion was even made that Ross might try throwing a shell overboard and listen for the sound of its explosion as it struck the sea bed, timing the interval between the shell's entry into the water and the moment that the explosion was heard.

Though oceanographic work was carried out when weather and sea conditions permitted, the instruments supplied were by no means standardised, nor were there persons trained in their use. In some cases the ship's captain made himself responsible for overseeing the work; in other instances the ship's surgeon (one who was likely to have had some academic training and who often made collections of plants and animals for the expedition) or an astronomer, assigned to make geophysical observations, kept records of

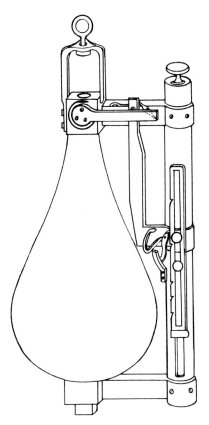

FIGURE 12 Davy's waterbottle

FIGURE 13 Marcet's first waterbottle

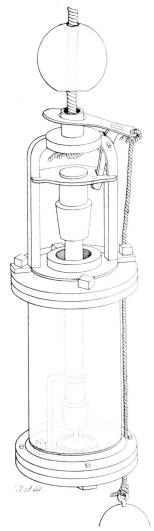

FIGURE 14 Marcet's second
waterbottle

sea depths and temperatures. It is not surprising that the need to
protect the Six's thermometer from the effects of pressure was not
fully appreciated at this time.

In deep water, the glass tube of a thermometer is compressed so
that the contained spirits or mercury rise, giving a false temperature
reading. Because of this, scientists believed that below a certain
level the sea temperature was a uniform 40°F. Six himself had
recommended making the marine thermometer of thicker glass but
this would have been of little help. Some observers did protect
their thermometers against the effect of pressure, albeit unwittingly,
by encasing them in filled watertight containers. This was done to
prevent breakages as the instrument was lowered and raised through
rough seas, a hazardous operation which could smash instruments
against the ship's side as she rolled and pitched. It meant however,
that the thermometer was insulated from the water that it was
supposed to measure, and it had therefore to be left down for a
considerable time in order that the whole apparatus could take up
the ambient temperature. Even then, the temperature structure of
a particular water column could not be determined with certainty,
as there was no way of telling exactly where the coldest and warm-
est layers occurred, except by a lengthy series of repeated operations, each going a little deeper than the preceding one. There was
seldom the time or opportunity for such work on expeditions or
voyages of exploration.

Since the Ross Antarctic Expedition, many more ships have been
sent to make their way through the ice and fogs of high latitudes.
Usually their main aim has been to set up a land base for geophysical observations. After 1925 the *Discovery* cruised regularly
in Antarctic waters to research on the life cycle of the whale populations, with a view to establishing a sustainable commercial yield
of whale oil. By the time of these voyages, in and after the latter
part of the 19th century, standardised instruments and apparatus
were issued to such ships, and the development of these will be
discussed in the next two sections.

Sounding voyages for laying telegraph cables, 1850–1900

Prior to 1850 it was thought that accurate deep-water soundings
could be made by increasing the weight of the lead relative to the
line, and this practice, first introduced in the US Navy and copied
by British and French officers, involved the use of a heavy weight
and a line made of silk, wire or twine. The weight, a 32 or 68 lb
cannon-ball, was rapidly run down from a ship's boat, and when
it was judged to have reached bottom, which was usually indicated
with certainty by a sudden change in the rate of running-out of the

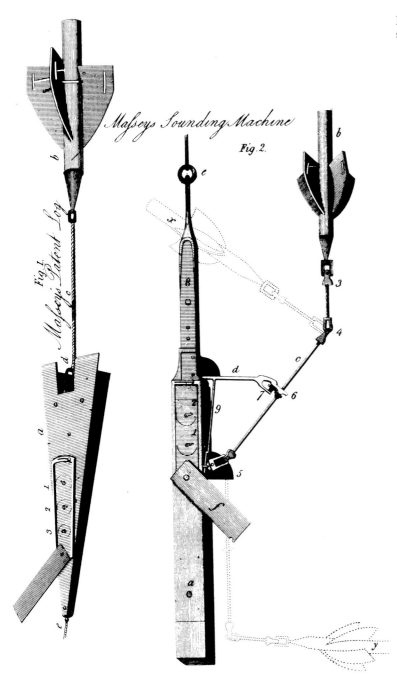

Masseys Sounding Machine

Fig. 2.

Fig. 1.

Masseys Patent Log

FIGURE 15 Massey waywiser
sounder

FIGURE 16 Burt's buoy and nipper

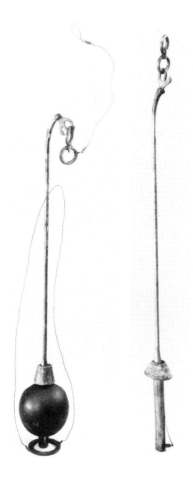

FIGURE 17 Brooke's detaching-weight sounder: complete (left) valved sampler rod (right)

line, the latter was cut at the surface and the depth calculated from the length of line remaining on the reel. The method was still inaccurate where submarine currents took the line sideways, on one occasion 17 km of wire was paid out without bottom being reached, in water that was no more than 6 km deep.

There were two other items employed in conjunction with sounding operations throughout much of the 19th century. The instrument-making firm of Edward Massey, which constructed ships' logs, adapted these for use as sounders. From the date of their first patent, in 1802, the Massey sounders went through various modifications but consisted basically of a vaned rotor which turned on descending through the water, driving a series of geared counting wheels. The apparatus was attached to a deep-sea lead, or carried on its own heavy plate (Figure 15). It was claimed that even with the sinker carried out of plumb, a mechanical sounder registered only the vertical distance travelled, and could even be used by a ship under way. The instrument worked well in moderately deep water and was valuable for checking line soundings where subsurface currents were suspected. It was not satisfactory in very deep water and its uncertainty was shared by all instruments involving metal moving parts. The machinery tended to jam under the enormous pressure. Similar sounders were made by the firms of Walker and Friend, both of whom made series of efficient logs.

In 1818 Peter Burt proposed another aid to sounding; the Buoy and Nipper. This device consisted of an inflatable canvas buoy, attached to a wooden and brass nipper through which the sounding line was passed (Figure 16). The line ran freely out through the nipper, being kept vertically over it by the buoy. When bottom was reached, the whole apparatus was hauled in, the nipper having clamped on the line, and the exact amount of line paid out could be calculated. The device proved very useful when sounding from a ship under way or drifting, as it did away with the need to lower a ship's boat. It was also found easier to use at night, when the dials on Massey's sounders were difficult to read.

The first submarine telegraph cable was laid in 1850 across the English Channel. The cable companies soon turned their efforts to getting a cable laid across the Atlantic in order to link Britain and America. For this they required closely-spaced accurate soundings along the prospective route, together with bottom samples and an indication of the temperatures to be encountered. Sufficient cable had to be made and laid so that it would rest flat on the sea bed, and not hang unsupported over rocky ground. The temperature measurement at the sea bed was needed as this affected the insulating qualities of the gutta-percha insulation placed round the copper core, and this in turn controlled the transmission rate of the telegraph signals. In the course of its length a cable might lay in shallow water of 20°C and pass into deep water of 0°C, such a range being common in the tropics.

During the early years of submarine cable-laying operations, these sounding voyages were undertaken by the Hydrographic

16

Offices of the British and American Navies, but before long the cable companies took over the work themselves, first chartering, then building, their own vessels for exploration and cable-laying.

In 1852 Ensign Brooke of the US Navy found an ingenious method of detaching at the bottom the weight used to take down a sounder. By this means, a light sampling tube accompanying the weight might be hauled up without breaking the line. The idea was by no means new, but had not been made practical in deep water. Brooke's sounder used as its weight a cannon ball bored through the centre and grooved on the outside. It rested on a ring suspended by cords passing along the grooves to a pivotted hook on the bracket to which the sounding line was spliced. The base of the sounder shaft was hollow and contained goose quills. The weight of the cannon-ball drove the shaft into the sediment, water escaping from the upper part of the shaft via a leather flap-valve. Sediment was forced into the quills. As the device hit the sea bed, the line slackened, the bracket pivotted, releasing the cannon-ball harness. On hauling up, ball and harness were left on the bottom, greatly reducing the weight to be lifted to the surface. One of the disadvantages of Brooke's sounder was the small quantity of sediment recovered. Also the delicate adjustment of the weight sometimes resulted in its dislodgement before reaching the sea bed, though Brooke himself overcame this by substituting a single hook for the two which he had originally employed.

The sounder was widely used by the US Navy and examples were also sent to Britain where it underwent various modifications and stimulated the invention of similar detaching devices (Figure 17). One of these was the set of 'claws' made by Carmelo Bonnici, ship's blacksmith on board HMS *Spitfire*, off Sevastopol in 1855 (Figure 18). Captain Spratt had previously used a silk line to sound to 1000 fathoms and hoped that with Bonnici's detacher he could leave the shot sinker at the bottom and retrieve a sea bed sample from similar depths.

Commander Mansell, running a line of soundings across the Eastern Mediterranean in HMS *Tartarus* in 1857 (Figure 19) found that with Brooke's sounder it was not easy to tell when bottom

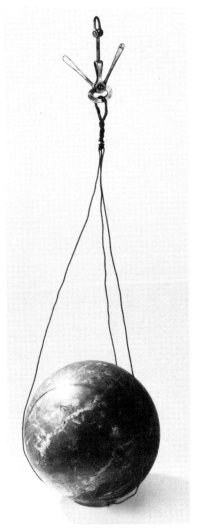

FIGURE 18 Bonnici's detaching claws and sinker weight
FIGURE 19 Chart and section of Mediterranean soundings, 1857

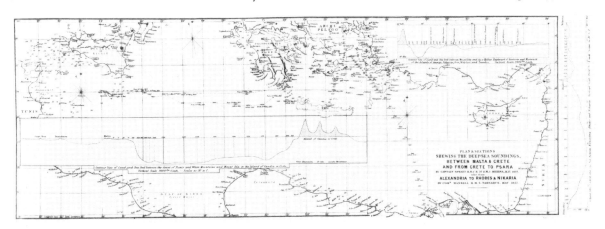

FIGURE 20 Skead's detaching weight sounder

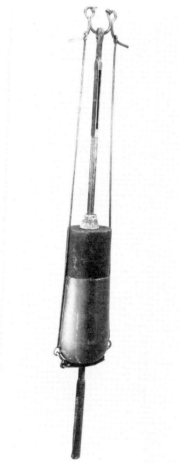

FIGURE 21 Dayman's modification of Brooke's sounder

had been reached, so that he overestimated the true depth of water. Bonnici's sounder also failed to collect a sample on some occasions. During a stay at Smyrna the ship's Master, Mr Skead, constructed another version of a detacher. This employed a 68 lb cannon-ball as sinker, carried in a harness similar to that of Bonnici. When the device reached the bottom, the detacher reversed, releasing the shot and itself striking the sea bed and thereby collecting a sediment sample on the tallow-armed lead cup. Skead's sounder was used in depths as great as 1500 fathoms, but like Bonnici's sounder, was not suitable for very deep water or on coarse sediments (Figure 20).

One of the most successful adaptations of Brooke's sounder was that made by Lt-Commander Joseph Dayman on board HMS *Cyclops* in 1857. The *Cyclops*, a steam frigate, was ordered to carry a line of soundings across the North Atlantic from Valencia in Ireland to Trinity Bay, Newfoundland, in preparation for a trans-atlantic cable. For this purpose it was important to have good bottom samples and Dayman modified the sounder by enlarging the cavity at the base of the rod and fitting a valve to it. He also used wire rods in place of the cord harness and he changed the weight from a sphere to a lead cylinder offering less resistance to the water. In this way he was able to make each sounding in a shorter time (Figure 21). Dayman took with him several Massey sounders and also used Burt's buoy and nipper. The following year HMS *Gorgon* with Dayman again in command made a survey of a transatlantic route via the Azores. This appeared less satisfactory as a cable line and in 1860 a northerly route via the Faeroes, Iceland and Greenland was surveyed by HMS *Bulldog*, commanded by Captain Sir Leopold McClintock.

The paddle-steamer *Bulldog* was issued with ten modified Brooke sounders and a large quantity of weights to be used with them. She made only a few soundings between the Hebrides and Iceland, but in each case these were found to indicate water much more shallow than appeared on the available charts. Around Greenland more soundings were made, especially at those places where the cable would have to be brought ashore. McClintock found that he was not getting adequate samples by means of the Brooke sounder, and accordingly his two Engineers Steil and Roughton, and Dr Wallich, the naturalist assigned to the ship, worked out a way of collecting a larger scoop from the sea bed. The resulting device, which became known as the Bulldog sounder, was appropriately named for it embodied a pair of scoops which were kept open by the weight of the sinker (Figure 22). On reaching bottom, the sinker fell away, and the scoops were closed by a rubber band. Provided that no stones were trapped between the jaws of the scoop, a fair sample from the top few inches of the sea bed was collected and brought up to the surface. Wallich subsequently took out two patents for this sounder, but before then it had been superseded by more sturdy and efficient apparatus, notably the Hydra and Baillie sounders which were used to such good purpose on the Challenger expedition, described in the following section. Two sounders made in France along similar lines were those known as the *Travailleur*, from the ship of that name, and the *sondeur à clef*. Both these employed a more positive closing valve to retain the sediment sample.

While clays and soft sediments were fairly easy to retrieve, shelly or stony deposits were not, such deposits often blocked the valves in the apparatus used. Where the bottom was rocky, the impact frequently damaged the sounding tube and nothing was recovered. By 1880 there was a clear divergence in the purpose of sounders: one branch of the family was developed more and more for the collection of samples, and larger grabs and corers were devised for this purpose to bring back not only mineral sediments but also the animal life which they contained. However, both these, and the devices intended purely for determining depth and retrieving small representative bottom samples were greatly improved by the change to wire line.

Attempts to sound with a wire line had been made as far back as the 1840s. The first US Government expedition under Captain Wilkes made some deep soundings between 1840 and 1842 using copper wire. Wire being so much thinner than hemp for a given strength took up much less space on board, a merit which became very apparent when stowing all the lines needed for apparatus shipped on long voyages of exploration. Sir William Thomson, (later Lord Kelvin) who became interested in deep sea sounding through his connection with the laying of submarine cables, made a trial in 1872 of a machine he had devised for sounding by means of a piano-wire line. His method, as eventually perfected, was to lead the sounding wire over a series of wheels, to one of which a resistance was applied, slightly exceeding the weight of wire in the water at any given moment. The wire therefore only ran out as long as the combined weight of wire and sinker exceeded the resistance. Once the sinker struck bottom, the resistance was greater than the suspended wire alone and the line ceased to be paid out. From a counter attached to one of the paying-out wheels the depth could be read off. This reading was instant and considerably more reliable than the method of noting rate-of-change in the paying out of hemp line (Figure 23).

Thomson's machine first saw active service on USS *Tuscarora* in the Pacific in 1873 under Commander Belknap. However, it was necessary to reel in the wire by hand to avoid jerks caused by the ship's motion. Lt-Commander Sigsbee modified Thomson's sounding machine during the winter of 1874–5 fitting an accumulator between the reel and the sinker to allow winding in by steam. The Sigsbee machine was used for three years on board the Coast Survey steamer *Blake* while on deep sea work in the Caribbean and northwest Atlantic. Sigsbee also introduced the stray-line, a short length of hemp from which the sounder itself hung. This avoided the risk of the wire kinking when it reached the bottom. Sigsbee made use of the same type of piano-wire as Thomson. This wire,

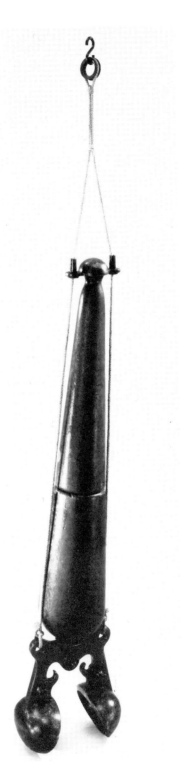

FIGURE 22 The *Bulldog* sounder-grab

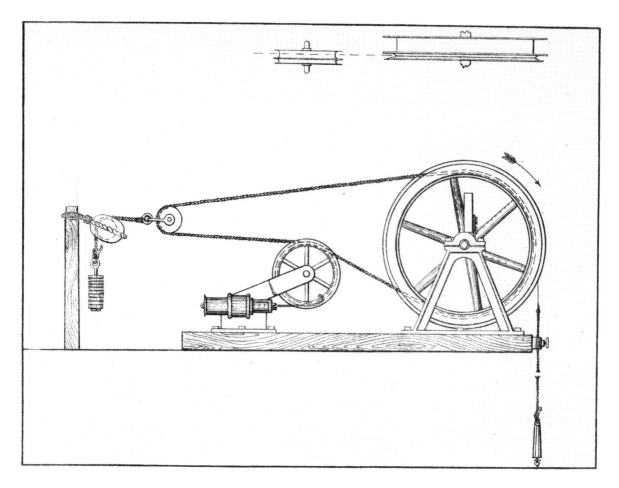

FIGURE 23 Sir William Thomson's sounding machine

weighing only 12 lbs per nautical mile in water, could take down a 100 lb shot and not only bring up the 14 lbs weight of the full collecting tube but carry besides thermometers for measuring temperature at the bottom and intermediate depths. Using the Belknap-Sigsbee detaching sounder which the two men developed for use with this machine, the time taken to reel in was generally below 1½ minutes per hundred fathoms, while the time to lower was only ½ minute per hundred fathoms. As a result of the speed at which soundings could be made Sigsbee, in his four years of command, sounded closely over the Gulf of Mexico, enabling the US Coast Survey to produce the first accurate chart which extended submarine topography from the shoreline out to deep water (Figure 24).

A similar machine was made on the British side of the Atlantic by F. R. Lucas, who as a youth had been in the *Great Eastern* for the laying of the first transatlantic cable. He introduced a sounding machine which was rather simpler than that of Sigsbee. The Hydrographic Office gave the first model a trial on HMS *Alert* under Captain Nares during 1878–9. Lucas, who became Chief Engineer to the Telegraph Construction and Maintenance Company, saw his machine become standard on most cable ships and naval surveying

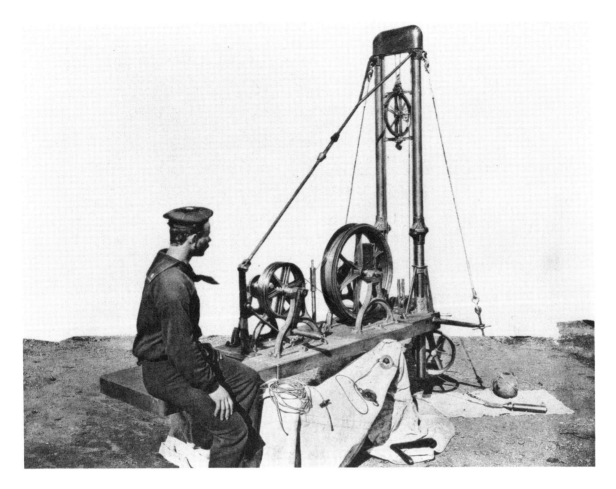

vessels, and in modified forms it continued in use until the 1960s. Both large and small versions were built, for deep and shallow sounding. Admiral Wharton described the Lucas machine in 1898 as having entirely superseded the use of hemp line for sounding. The wire used was galvanised, and as supplied in standard 5000 fathom lengths, had a breaking strain of 240 lbs. Thinner wire could be supplied for making especially deep soundings in order to accommodate a longer amount on the reel (Figure 25).

Much of the sounding work done by telegraph companies was in moderate depths of water on the continental shelves. The individual requirements of each area, often geologically distinct, led to a proliferation of sounder types which could be used on the Lucas sounding machine. Closely-spaced soundings were essential where the bottom was steeply sloping or breached by underwater canyons, and several of the sounders were designed to work with the ship under way (Figure 26).

Other methods of sounding were put forward: Sir William Thomson designed several pressure-sounders which relied on the depth pressure to force water into a tube graduated in fathoms. His alternative method of registering was to coat the tube with silver chromate. The distance to which the water had been forced was

FIGURE 24 Sigsbee's sounding machine, used on the US Coast Survey steamer *Blake*

marked by the line dividing dry red chromate from a white deposit resulting from the decomposition of the chromate by seawater. Both these Thomson sounding machines were popular in the late 19th century; in moderately deep water they allowed soundings to be taken with the ship under way. However, they, and others like them, served the purposes of navigation rather than of oceanography.

The cable surveys also had to take account of sea-bed temperatures. When the first of these surveys were in progress, carried out by the Navy's Hydrographic Department, a variety of thermometers were available, none of which was really satisfactory. Captain Hoskyn, who took *Porcupine* to the area west of Ireland in 1862 to extend Dayman's survey of 1857, took several sounders (including the Bulldog); two pressure-gauges, and metallic and common deep-sea thermometers. At each station he sent down two

FIGURE 25 Lucas sounding machine

Sherlock's detacher for sinkers

Where a bottom sample was not required the line could be carried down by a weight which was detached as it hit the sea bed. Reeling-in could then be done at speed as the ship steamed to her next station. Mr Sherlock, who invented this detacher, was Chief Engineer on the cable ship *Electra*.

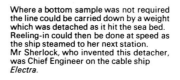

Lucas snapper sounders

For use in shallow water weights up to 30 lb were used, both sinker and sampler being recovered. In deeper water heavier sinker weights were fitted and detached at the bottom. The jaws of the snappers are held open until the bottom is struck, when they are closed by a spring.

Silvertown and Stallibrass sounding tubes

These two tubes were similar in construction; the larger central section of the tube brought up a sample of bottom water while the three small tubes underneath collected a sediment sample.

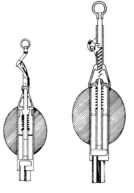

In the Silvertown sounder the wire sling holding the weights was cut by a self-acting knife as the line was hauled up. This had the advantage that the weight was utilised to push the tubes well into the bottom. However, if the sediment was very soft the whole device might penetrate so far that the knife failed to operate. Edward Stallibrass produced a version that recovered a 1-litre water sample and had a slipping-hook to detach the weight.

Driver sounder

This device was used by the Admiralty Hydrographic service. It could be made by a ship's blacksmith, using gas piping. It recovered a bottom sample up to 2 feet long, retained by a double flap valve at the bottom of the tube. The wire retaining the weights was slipped as the sounder struck bottom.

FIGURE 26 Grab and corer samplers used on sounding machines.

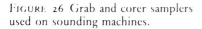

lines, one carrying the sounder, the other with thermometers and other instruments fastened at intervals along it.

Johnson's metallic thermometer (Figure 27) had as its element bimetallic strips of brass and steel. As these strips flexed under changing temperature they moved an index across a graduated dial and also pushed pins to the extremes of temperature reached. Johnson believed that his thermometer did not require any pressure correction but like most mechanical devices it was unreliable in deep water, and it was eventually rejected in favour of liquid thermometers with pressure-protected bulbs.

In 1857 Admiral Fitzroy and James Glaisher suggested to the instrument-makers Negretti & Zambra that the Six thermometer be modified by enclosing its bulb within a glass sheath partly filled with mercury, to relieve pressure on the inner bulb. This version of a pressure-protected thermometer was less successful than the later Miller-Casella pattern, (described below) for its length made it fragile. Only fifty were made and these were issued to the hydrographic ships of the Navy (Figure 28).

The Six thermometer's prime disadvantage was that, though it registered minimum temperature, it was impossible to tell the depth at which this coldest water lay. There were lesser problems: if handled roughly (and this was almost impossible to avoid during rough weather) the indexes shifted; if carried horizontally the mercury became mixed with the alcohol. For the purposes of cable-laying it was the sea-bed temperature that was important, and so it was often preferable to take the temperature of a mass of sediment hauled up from the bottom, much as John Ross had done half a century earlier.

To get round these problems, Negretti and Zambra brought out in 1874 a completely new type of deep sea thermometer. Whereas the Six thermometer required careful handling, the Negretti instrument worked on the principle of registering the temperature by upsetting, or reversing, the thermometer. The protected-bulb thermometer was in the shape of an inverted U. At the required depth the thermometer reversed, causing the mercury to pass into the other limb of the tube. At the same time a small glass plug floated into the neck of the siphon, preventing any more mercury emerging from the bulb, whatever the subsequent temperature. The first instruments were fixed to a weighted wooden block, so that they reversed by the simple action of being hauled in, but soon this was replaced by more positive methods: the thermometer was overturned within a frame, actuated by a propeller as the frame was raised, thereby releasing the capsizing spring (Figure 29). Alternatively, when faster reversing was needed (such as in shallow water) a trigger mechanism could be used, worked by sending a messenger down the line from the ship (Figure 30). Many versions of the reversing thermometer were made in other European countries, now all involved in cable-laying and oceanographic research. With a constriction in the tube immediately above the bulb, the thermometer could be made in a straight, rather than U-shaped form,

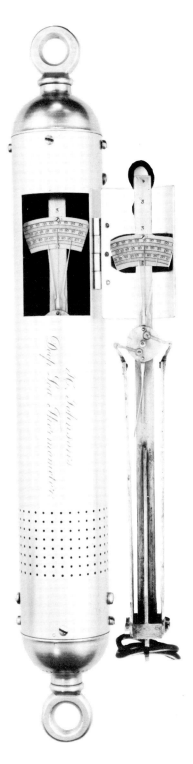

FIGURE 27 Johnson's bimetallic thermometer. The thermometer element (right). The thermometer in its case (left).

23

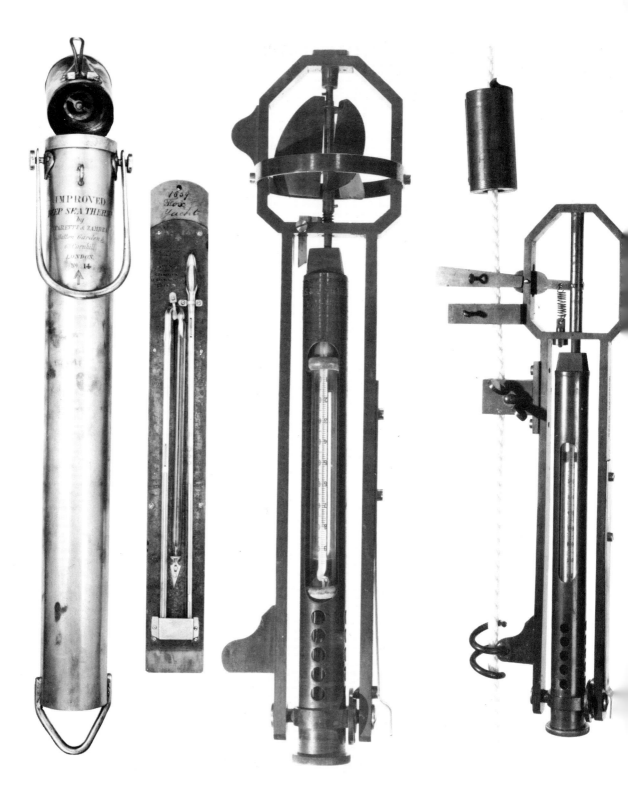

FIGURE 28 Negretti & Zambra
max-min thermometer, with its
Jamieson case.

FIGURE 29 Negretti & Zambra
reversing thermometer in a
Magnaghi frame

FIGURE 30 Negretti & Zambra
reversing thermometer in a 'Scottish
Pattern' frame

24

and it continues today to be the standard type of thermometer for use with waterbottles.

William Siemens, whose family were closely involved with all aspects of telegraphy, constructed an electrical thermometer which was tried out on USS *Blake* in 1881 (Figure 31). Siemens considered that the principle whereby the electrical resistance of a conductor varied with its temperature might be applied to the construction of a thermometer. In essence, the apparatus consisted of a coil of wire sunk to the required depth, and coupled by connecting wires to form one arm of a Wheatstone's bridge. The other arm was a comparison coil, immersed in a water tank on the deck. The temperature of this water was adjusted until the bridge balanced, at which point the tank water was identical in temperature with the seawater round the submerged coil. The apparatus proved difficult to operate when the ship was rolling, and it also required the provision of ice to adjust the temperature of water in the tank. It did enable the serial measurements to be closely spaced as the observations could be made quite quickly. Various instruments proposed around this period employed electrical registration, but they all suffered from the lack of a conducting cable strong enough to be used in the conditions encountered at sea. In fact, the passive submarine telegraph cable itself, laying on the sea bed, did by its varying resistance from day to day indicate the average temperature of the water which covered it.

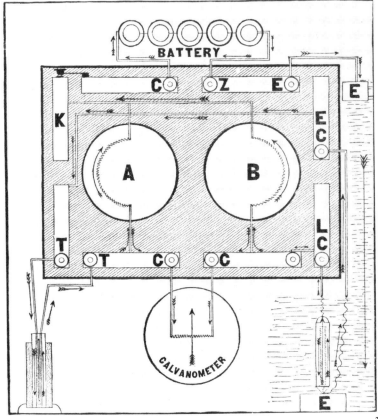

FIGURE 31 Diagram of the electrical circuit of Siemens' deep sea thermometer

The search for life in the depths

Coastal people have always exploited marine plants, shellfish, fishes and whales as a source of food and as useful materials. Successful fisherman were familiar with the life cycles of these animals but it was in their own interest to keep this knowledge a secret. When marine biology became an accepted field of study it was the nets and dredges used by fisherman that were first used by the scientists. Marsigli himself used a common oyster dredge.

In 1779 Otho Müller, a Danish zoologist, invented a naturalists' dredge having a net attached to a square frame, and this he used successfully in the coastal waters of Denmark, in depths up to 30 fathoms. Dredging in shallow water was so easy, and its results so interesting, that many naturalists were encouraged to turn their attention to the study of marine life.

Deep-water dredging, on the other hand, was not so easily undertaken. For towing the dredge across the sea bed a very thick rope was required, and the whole assemblage was very heavy to lift, especially on the frequent occasions that the dredge collected a load of mud or stones. John Ross, on his second Arctic voyage, 1829–33, was able to dredge only to 70 fathoms as he was dependent on manpower to turn the capstan hauling in the line, though his vessel was itself steam-powered. On this, and other occasions, starfish and brittle-stars were sometimes brought up on the deepsea sounding line, from much greater depths. There were, however, arguments as to whether such creatures had truly been collected from the bottom, or had attached themselves to the line on its passage through intermediate levels.

The great importance of dredging as a means of zoological research was recognised in 1839 by the British Association, which appointed a committee to extend the techniques available and begin plotting the geographical distribution of the various classes of animals.

One of the most eminent marine zoologists of the time, Professor Edward Forbes (1815–54), conducted long and patient investigations into the bathymetrical distribution of marine life. Working originally in the seas around Britain, he later extended his studies to the eastern Mediterranean where he joined the hydrographic survey ship *Beacon*. He was able to define various zones, noting that plants grew only where sunlight penetrated the water. Finding that the number of animal species and their populations diminished with increasing depth, he thought that life was probably absent below 300 fathoms in the Mediterranean Sea. However, judging from the reports of Arctic expeditions, the boundary appeared to lie deeper in polar seas.

At this time James Clark Ross was sent to the Antarctic with the ships *Erebus* and *Terror*. The cruise, which lasted from 1839 to 1843, was devoted to exploring and charting the coasts of Antarctica, to making geophysical observations, and to carrying out marine research when ice and weather permitted. Ross succeeded in dredging under 400 fathoms of water, and on every haul was rewarded with a diversity of life.

As the same species of animals were found at both poles, and always in water of a similar temperature, Ross suggested that it would be possible for them to occupy the intervening seas also, providing that the range of temperature across the sea bed did not exceed 5°F. In general, this concept of a *near*-uniform bottom temperature was later shown to be correct.

By mid-century dredging operations had extended to temperate waters. In 1846 Captain Spratt dredged a rich haul of creatures from 310 fathoms in the course of his hydrographic survey in the western Mediterranean. The naturalist Michael Sars published in 1850 a list of thirteen species that he had discovered living some 300 fathoms down off the Norwegian coast.

As noted in an earlier section, sounding lines could be worked through deeper water than dredges. When Brooke's sounder, and others like it, came into regular use on the cable-sounding explorations, a whole new range of bottom-sediment samples became available for study. Microscope examination revealed that many mud samples recovered from deep water were composed of minute shells, or tests, of Foraminifera. Great debate arose as to whether these tiny organisms lived on the sea bed where they were found, or at the surface or intermediate levels, whence their empty shells fell to collect in drifts at the bottom of the sea.

The existence of life in the depths was soon to be confirmed. In 1857 a telegraph cable was laid in the Mediterranean between Sardinia and the coast of North Africa. During 1860 parts of it were pulled up for repair. Some 40 miles of cable were recovered, from the Sardinian end, from waters up to 1200 fathoms deep. Where the cable had laid in shallow water, penetrated by the sun's rays, it was covered with seaweed, and throughout the length examined it had been colonised by molluscs, corals and other forms of sedentary life. Undeniably these had grown to maturity fixed to the cable as it lay on the sea bed (Figure 32).

FIGURE 32 Portion of submarine telegraph cable on which marine organisms once lived

FIGURE 33 Dredge used from HMS *Porcupine*

In 1868 the Royal Society laid before the Admiralty a statement of the advantages to be gained from a short dredging cruise in the North Atlantic. The Admiralty responded by placing the surveying ship HMS *Lightning* at the disposal of Professor Wyville Thomson and Dr W. B. Carpenter during the autumn of the same year.

Lightning was the oldest paddle-steamer in the Royal Navy. She was a leaky old vessel and kept the water out imperfectly, while the bad weather encountered during the six-week cruise made conditions very hard for all on board. The ship sailed from Pembroke via the Hebrides to the Faeroe Islands, returning with a detour out into the open North Atlantic Ocean. The results showed beyond question that life was varied and abundant, represented by all the invertebrate groups, at depths in the ocean down to 650 fathoms, the deepest point reached by the dredge.

Another important fact emerged; instead of deep water having a uniform temperature of 4°C, great masses of water of different temperature were found to be in slow movement, each contributing to a grand system of oceanic circulation, and each characterised by a distinctive fauna.

Finally, a large proportion of the deep-sea species taken were hitherto unknown to science, while others were identical to fossil forms known from the Chalk and older rocks that had been originally laid down on the sea bed.

So much of value had resulted from the seventeen dredgings made on board HMS *Lightning* that the Admiralty agreed to provide another vessel, HMS *Porcupine*, to enable the series to continue during the summer months of 1869 and 1870.

In addition to the temperature observations which had turned out to be so interesting, it was decided to make chemical analyses of the seawater. For this purpose *Porcupine's* chartroom was fitted out as a laboratory and a chemist joined the two naturalists on board.

Porcupine was a far more seaworthy craft than the old *Lightning*, and under the direction of Captain Calver her crew soon became adept at handling the heavy dredge. Three separate cruises, each with its own scientific team, were made during 1869. The first covered an area to the west of Ireland, going as far north as the Rockall Bank. The second cruise went south to the Bay of Biscay, while the third went to the same stations covered by the *Lightning* cruise, in order to carry out the seawater analyses not previously undertaken.

During the first cruise the dredge was made to work successfully 1470 fathoms down, again bringing up a varied haul of invertebrates. This led the scientists to direct the second voyage into the Bay of Biscay, the closest area where deeper water could be found. Two hauls were obtained in water over 2000 fathoms deep. The whole operation at these stations took about eight hours. The heaviest of their dredge-frames, weighing 225 lbs, was used here. It was 4 ft 6 inches across, with a 6 inch-wide opening. The frame carried an outer bag of strong twine netting and an inner fine-wove lining. At Captain Calver's suggestion a long transverse iron bar was fixed to the rear end of the bag and on this were hung several hemp swabs, of the type which the sailors used to swab the decks. These tangles collected the small creatures which, half buried in mud or wedged between stones, might otherwise be missed as the dredge passed over them. On the towing part of the frame a weak link was fitted, in order that the main towing rope would not break should the dredge become fast between rocks. As the link snapped, the frame was jolted sideways and this normally served to free the dredge (Figure 33).

The hemp dredging rope was 3000 fathoms long, of which the third nearest the dredge was 2 inches in circumference and the rest 2½ inches. 2 cwts of sinkers were attached 500 fathoms from the dredge in order to speed its descent through the water, A derrick was rigged up, sometimes at the port bow, sometimes, as shown here (Figure 34), at the stern. The illustration shows the accumulator, a set of strong rubber bands held between two boards, which acted as a shock-absorber to prevent the rope breaking under the strains of the pitching and rolling of the ship.

The vessel then towed and drifted for several hours so that the dredge moved slowly across the sea bed. The donkey-engine on deck was used to haul up the rope; this operation took almost four hours to accomplish as the total weight of rope and dredge, even in the water, was 2042 lbs.

During the cruise in HMS *Lightning*, Wyville Thomson had made use of registering thermometers of the Six type: a U-shaped tube having one limb terminating in a large bulb entirely filled with a mixture of creosote and water, which acted as the thermometric fluid.* A registering segment of mercury occupied the lower part of the U, and the other limb ended in a smaller bulb partly filled with the creosote mixture together with its vapour and some air. The indexes were of steel with a hair spring, and they floated on the mercury surface, being left behind at the highest point reached by the mercury within each limb. Beyond a very limited depth, pressure falsified the reading, and corrections were required.

Trials were made on this occasion of a standard Admiralty (Hydrographic Office pattern) thermometer and others by different makers. These were found to give widely varying results when sent to a few hundred fathoms. When the cruise was over, the Deep-Sea Committee of the Royal Society met at the Hydrographic Office where the Society's Vice-President, Dr W. A. Miller, made proposals for a pressure-resistant thermometer.

In collaboration with L. P. Casella, the instrument maker, a satisfactory method of achieving this was eventually devised. The full bulb of the thermometer was surrounded by an outer glass sheath, the space between the two being filled with a mixture of alcohol, its vapour, and some air. This mixture yielded to the pressure of the water, thereby relieving the thermometer bulb itself. The so-called Miller-Casella thermometer proved very successful,

FIGURE 34 The stern derrick of HMS *Porcupine*, showing the dredge ready for lowering and, (right) the accumulator which took the strain off the sounding line as the ship pitched.

* Creosote preserved the elasticity of the index hair-springs.

29

and was employed on the *Porcupine* cruises and on many other expeditions thereafter (Figure 35).

For use at sea the thermometer was mounted on an ebonite block and provided with a porcelain scale. The whole assembly was protected by a copper case whose ends were pierced by holes to allow the water to pass freely through. To determine the temperature profile of the water throughout its depth *serial* soundings were made. This required a measured quantity of line to be run out and the lead and thermometer hauled in each time. It was a tedious business; one serial sounding in the Bay of Biscay where the temperature was measured every 50 fathoms down to 850 fathoms occupied the crew for an entire day.

FIGURE 35 Miller-Casella thermometer

The naturalists needed to know the exact depth to which their thermometers and dredges were sent. For this purpose two sounders were used. In 1868 the Fitzgerald sounder, invented that year, gave unfailing service. This simple apparatus was lowered in the position shown in the illustration (Figure 36). When it struck bottom, and the strain came off the rope, the vertical metal arm slipped sideways, detaching its weight and driving the scoop into the sea bed. On hauling up, the apparatus fell into a nearly vertical line with the full scoop coming up in the middle, its mouth closed against the lid.

On board the *Porcupine*, having need to sound to greater depths, they made use of the Hydra sounder, invented the previous year aboard the surveying vessel of that name. Inspired by the Brooke detaching sounder, the Hydra apparatus was very sturdy, and capable of carrying three hundredweights of sinker. It collected a small sample of bottom water which was held in the tube above the sediment plug, the latter retained by a butterfly valve. This arrangement worked well only on fine-grained sediments. However, on this occasion it was of little consequence as the dredge was sent down at every station and itself brought up abundance of material from the sea bed.

The sounder was used from the stern derrick, in conjunction with an accumulator, and usually went down accompanied by two thermometers and a water bottle, lashed a fathom or two above it. On the deepest sounding, that of 2435 fathoms, it took 33 minutes to reach the bottom and two hours 2 minutes to haul, with the aid of the donkey engine. Wyville Thomson reported that even at this great depth, nearly three miles, the shock of the weight striking the bottom was distinctly perceptible to Captain Calver, who kept his hand on the line as it went down.

The water bottle used on the two *Porcupine* cruises (Figure 37) was not as reliable as the naturalists might have wished. The brass cylinder, holding just over a litre and a half of water, was closed at each end by a brass disc, in the centre of which was a ground conical plug. On descent, the flow of water kept the valves open, and when the bottle was hauled up the valves closed on the water which had entered at the greatest depth reached. In practice it proved extremely difficult to lower the bottle with the rapid steady motion needed to keep the valves fully open, and any hesitation while the bottle was being raised resulted in dilution of its contents.

By 1870 a true science of the sea had come into being. In 1865 Professor Forchammer of Copenhagen published the results of twenty years of patient work analysing seawater from all parts of the world. American and British vessels ran sounding surveys around the continental margins and over those ocean crossings of commercial importance (but not, as yet, across the Pacific Ocean.) From 1867 American biologists undertook research every summer on conditions within the Gulf Stream, while the British ships *Lightning* and *Porcupine* had shown what could be achieved with a modest programme and reliable apparatus. A new concept of ocean-

FIGURE 36 Fitzgerald or *Lightning* sounder

FIGURE 37 Brass valved
waterbottle, used on *Porcupine*

ography began to take shape, in which the whole body of water underwent a gradual circulation, and in whose depth various creatures were to be found, notwithstanding the extreme conditions which greatly hindered investigation.

In 1871 Dr Carpenter drew the attention of the Royal Society to the fact that other nations were now embarking on large-scale physical and biological investigations of the oceans, and that Britain should participate in this work. The Austro-Hungarian empire had already organised a round-the-world cruise by the *Novara* between 1857 and 1859. The *Novara* was sent partly to 'show the flag' but also undertook a modest scientific programme and, perhaps more importantly, the results of this were published in 24 volumes, in 1862, thereby making available to the scientific community all the data so carefully gathered.

The Royal Society drew up a plan, to which the Admiralty agreed, by which a ship and crew, together with a scientific staff, should visit the several oceans and extend existing knowledge of the deep seas. A comprehensive programme of physical and chemical investigation of the waters and bottom deposits, together with a study of all organic life in the areas visited, was drawn up, and the government agreed to produce the necessary funds.

The ship selected for the cruise was HMS *Challenger*, a steam corvette of 2306 tons. *Challenger* underwent an extensive refit with laboratories and workrooms replacing her armaments, while space was found for cabins for the scientific staff and to stow the many miles of rope needed for sounding and dredging, as well as all the scientific apparatus and the samples that would be collected (Figure 38).

Across the central part of the upper deck a platform was built from which dredging and trawling operations could be carried out and upon which the dredge contents could be emptied. The naturalists were able to sieve through the mud to collect specimens without hampering the sailors working the ship (Figure 39).

For dredging, *Challenger* carried three sizes of hemp rope, the largest being three inches in circumference. The rope currently being used was stored in racks in the forecastle. Trawling and dredging were carried out from the mainyard with the rope rove through an accumulator larger than that used for sounding as the strains encountered by the dredge-rope were much greater.

Soundings were made from platforms projecting outwards from each side abreast the foremast. The sails were furled and the ship brought under steam head-to-wind. The sounding line was carried through an accumulator and various sounders were used, according to the anticipated depth to be plumbed.

With a few exceptions, *Challenger* did not take on board any new apparatus for physical oceanography. In view of her long programme, when she would be far from home, it was considered best to rely on tried and tested instruments and to use hemp rope, although wire was being used for sounding by other expeditions at this time.

FIGURE 38 Zoology laboratory on board HMS *Challenger* (above) Chemistry laboratory on board HMS *Challenger* (above left). A Buchanan waterbottle stands by the chair and thermometer cases hang by the door.

FIGURE 39 Dredging gear on board HMS *Challenger*

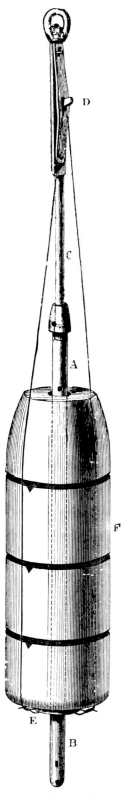

FIGURE 40 The *Hydra* sounder

For sounding, when the depth was expected to be less than 1000 fathoms a tube lead or a cup lead was used, according to the nature of the bottom. When the depth of water exceeded 1000 fathoms the Hydra sounder was used, with the necessary number of iron sinker weights (Figure 40). After *Challenger* sailed, the Baillie sounder became available and 12 of these were sent out to the ship in 1873 (Figure 41). These were more sturdy than the Hydra sounders, and had a slightly different detaching mechanism. They proved capable of sounding on every occasion that they were used, though in very deep water this was a slow task. Keeping the ship exactly at the spot where the sounder entered the water, the line was run out, noting the time that each 100-fathom mark entered the water. This interval increased regularly with depth, until a sudden lengthening of intervals indicated that bottom had been reached and the sounder was no longer dragging the line down. With 3 cwt sinker weights it could take well over one hour for the sounder to reach bottom in 4000 fathoms.

The thermometer used for almost all the observations made from *Challenger* was the Miller-Casella version of the Six registering thermometer, fitted into a copper case for protection. Several of these were usually lashed to the sounding line, a fixed distance apart. During the course of the voyage, Negretti & Zambra patented a reversing thermometer and several of these were sent out to the ship and used with some success. The frames which held the reversing mechanism proved unreliable and so they were modified on board. The Negretti thermometer also had its bulb protected from the effects of pressure by an outer glass sheath, but in this case the intervening space was half-filled with mercury (Figure 42).

Two types of waterbottle were used to recover samples of seawater for analysis – the slip bottle shown here operated on reaching the bottom (Figure 43) while to obtain samples of the intermediate water the stop-cock bottle was employed. This bottle was lowered with the stop-cocks open, and the water passing freely through it. When the requisite depth had been reached the line was checked, hauled in a few fathoms, then let go, checked again at the same mark, and finally hauled in altogether by the donkey engine. By this means the flap passed through a horizontal position closing the stop-cocks, and then fell flat against the side of the bottle, carrying with it a spring-loaded locking rod.

Under the command of Captain G. S. Nares, *Challenger* left England on 21 December 1872. Her five scientific staff were supervised by Dr Wyville Thomson, at that time Professor of Natural History at Edinburgh University. On her way around the world, the ship passed through all except the Arctic regions carrying out investigations on the deep seas, at isolated oceanic islands, in shallow tropical seas and down towards the permanent ice of Antarctica. She sailed in all 68 890 miles, obtained 492 soundings, 263 serial temperature soundings and made 133 dredgings and 151 trawls. South of Japan the *Challenger* made her deepest sounding:

4475 fathoms. This depth was confirmed by two separate sounding operations. On the first occasion one of the thermometers sent down was shattered by the pressure, and the second time both thermometers were broken.

The cruise of the *Challenger* established a range of values for the world's oceans, and the comprehensive reports on every aspect of the scientific work undertaken, which included zoology, botany, meteorology and geophysics, as well as oceanography, were published as a series of 50 volumes between the years 1880 and 1895.

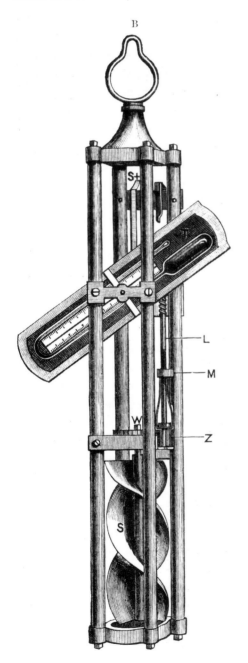

FIGURE 42
Negretti & Zambra
reversing thermometer
fitted into a frame
which reversed it
through 360°

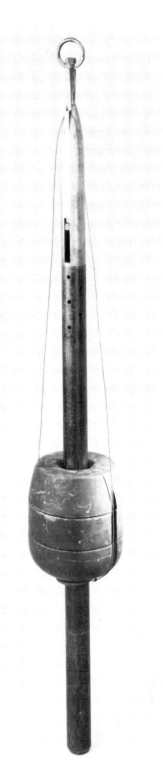

FIGURE 41 The Baillie sounder, similar to the *Hydra* in design but much sturdier

35

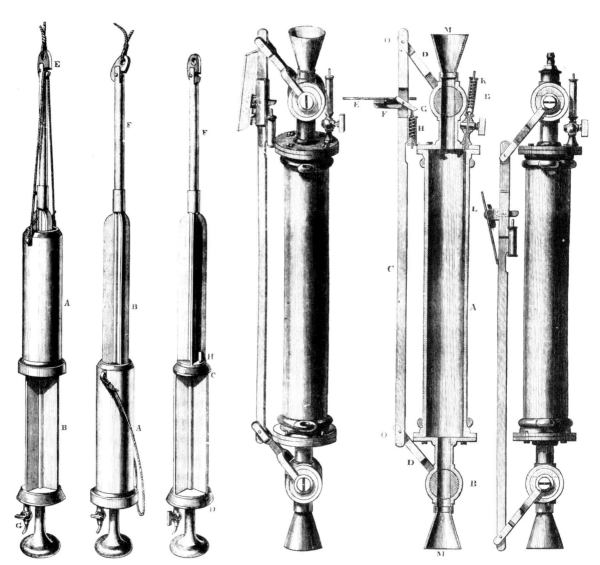

FIGURE 43 The Slip waterbottle
(left) for collecting water from the
sea bottom. Buchanan's Stopcock
waterbottle (right), for collecting
mid-water samples

International fisheries research

The need for scientific fisheries research did not arise until the last decades of the 19th century. During that time in Britain a number of Commissions had listened to evidence from fishermen on the failure of some fisheries and on the destructive effects of particular forms of gear. In the North Sea the decisive event was the introduction of the steam trawler in the 1880s. These trawlers were more efficient than sailing smacks because they worked independently of wind and tide, used powerful steam winches, and employed otter-trawls rather than beam-trawls. By the end of the 19th century more than 600 steam trawlers were working out of British ports, and similar fleets were being built in European ports. The fish stock declined by one-third within the North Sea, and in many other areas it failed completely.

It was realised that the scientific and economic importance of the results of research in the Baltic, the North Sea, and the North Atlantic would be greatly extended if this could be carried out on an international basis. Accordingly, in 1902, the International Council for the Exploration of the Sea was established by the nations surrounding the Baltic and North Sea. The Council's headquarters was in Copenhagen and a laboratory was set up in Kristiania (now the city of Oslo) to improve and standardise apparatus used by the research vessels of member countries, to provide samples of Standard Sea Water for comparative analysis, and to determine the best methods for measuring salinity, temperature, the presence of plankton (on which many fish feed) and so forth. The Council recommended two main lines of research: firstly the problem of exploitation of stocks, and secondly the effects of the environment on stock variability. In subsequent years, up to the present time, treaties of conservation have been signed between the various groups of countries concerned.

International cooperation is essential in fisheries research and in legislation to conserve stocks. The fish spawn in certain well-defined areas but may be caught at maturity far from their breeding-grounds. During the course of a year large fish may migrate up to 3000 km, travelling with tidal and oceanic currents in search of their food, while many smaller fish also migrate 100 to 200 km each year. The direction and extent of their travel will depend on the temperature of the water and the availability of their food and both vary widely from one year to the next. Fisheries research attempts to discover the cause of this variation and, if possible, to predict for the benefit of fishermen where mature stocks of fish are likely to be found at a given time.

From the beginning, vessels contributing to the ICES programme worked within a limited area, taking closely-spaced observations over long periods of time. The emphasis was very much on monitoring water quality and water movement, and for this purpose capacious water bottles and sensitive current meters were required.

Until the late 19th century the measurement of currents had always been somewhat inaccurate. Timed drifters and propeller-driven mechanical logs gave only a rough indication of the *relative* motion between ship and water, unless the vessel was securely anchored to the sea bed. Measurements made with the ship riding to a sea-anchor were totally misleading since they depended on the assumption that a current was flowing only at the surface, or only at depth, whereas this is seldom the case.

In 1876 Lieutenant J. E. Pillsbury constructed the first current meter which was capable of registering the speed and direction of subsurface currents, for use in the US Coast and Geodetic Survey investigations of the Gulf Stream. He made further improvements to the meter during the 1880s and it came into use on American and some British hydrographical survey vessels by the end of the century (Figure 44).

The accuracy of Pillsbury's meter was largely due to his system of anchoring in deep water, as shown (Figure 45). The meter having been lowered to the required depth, it was set in motion by the release of a messenger down the line which struck a metal plate and

FIGURE 44 Pillsbury's current meter

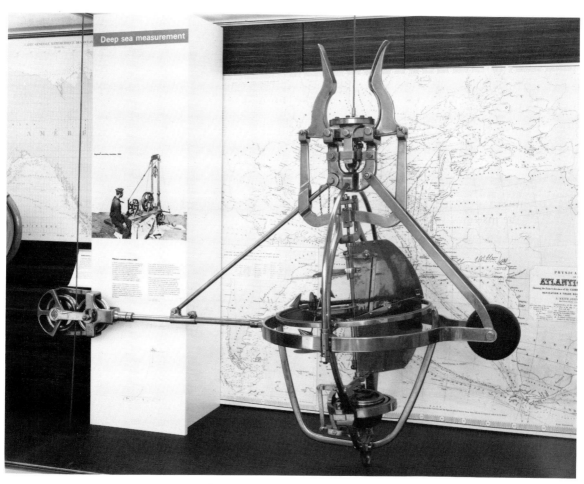

freed the mechanism. The rudder was then able to take up the direction of the current, the small cones revolved on their axis and the compass needle took up a north-south line.

After a measured time-interval a second messenger was sent down which locked all parts of the machinery. When the meter was recovered the number of revolutions made by the cones could be used to calculate the speed of the current while its direction was given by the angle between the compass needle and the rudder.

The Pillsbury meter was deliberately made very heavy so that the instrument itself would not be deflected sideways by the current which it was intended to measure. A much lighter apparatus, intended for work at moderate depths below the ship, was developed around 1905 by V. W. Ekman as part of the ICES laboratory programme. An eight-vaned propeller was turned by the current flow, and was geared to a series of counters. Light tail-fins turned the meter to face into the current. Once the meter had been lowered and set running by the release of a messenger down the line, the direction which it had taken up was registered in a most ingenious fashion: a compass with a grooved needle was mounted on the instrument, and a hopper regulated by the propeller released lead shot at intervals. This was directed by the compass needle into one of the 36 compartments forming the compass bowl, thereby indicating the alignment that the meter had taken up in the current, with respect to magnetic north. This meter underwent several modifications and was used extensively for many years.

A current meter which measures velocity by means of a propeller does not function well where currents are weak or fluctuating. In 1900 Professor Fridtjof Nansen began trials with a meter which employed a suspended pendulum displaced from the vertical according to the direction and strength of the current. This type of meter was used either lowered from a ship, or secured to a tripod resting on the sea bed (Figure 46). Movement of the pendulum was scribed onto the concave plate which was freshly coated with wax each time the instrument was used.

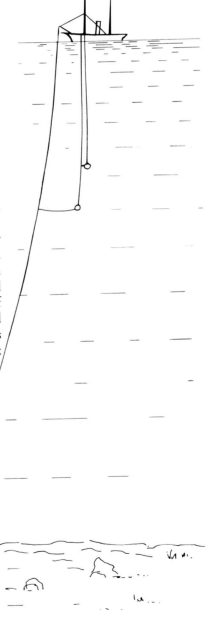

FIGURE 45 Pillsbury's method of anchoring the ship in deep water and running his meter down a jackstay line to keep it vertical.

FIGURE 46 Nansen's pendulum
current meter

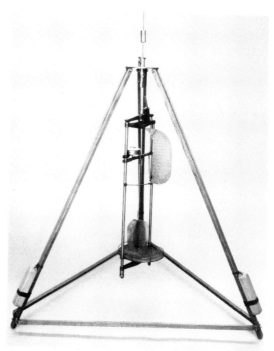

FIGURE 47 Carruthers' drift
indicator

Each of the three meters referred to above give only single value readings. One way in which the Ekman meter could be employed to give long-term measurements was in the form of the drift indicator developed by J. Carruthers around 1935 (Figure 47). The indicator showed the proportion of time that a current had been flowing in different directions. In shallow water the extent to which rate and direction of flow vary with season and under changing wind and tide conditions is of importance in fisheries research because of the influence of drift on the survival and migration of young fish stocks. The Carruthers drift indicator was suspended from a vessel or a lightship for periods of 74½ hours, i.e. through several tidal cycles. The cups at the top of the instrument regulated the release of balls from a hopper. As in the Ekman meter, these were directed along a grooved compass needle into compartments below. By counting the number of balls in the various compartments the proportion of time the current had been flowing in each direction could be calculated, and the residual drift calculated.

FIGURE 48 Fjelstad recording current meter

To obtain continuous recording of the velocity and direction of current flow, mechanical, photographic and electrical registration were all tried out, as well as wireless transmission of data. Mechanical methods did not always require the mechanism to be sealed from the water whereas the use of clockwork and photographic papers did, making the apparatus far more complex.

A simple means of obtaining a series of readings was devised by J. E. Fjelstad in 1949. His meter incorporated a metallic tape, onto which the number of counted propeller revolutions, and the compass direction of the alignment of the instrument, was stamped each time that a messenger was released down the line (Figure 48).

The general direction of surface drift may be observed by the movement of floating objects. It had been long the policy of ship's captains to release bottles containing a note of the date and ship's position, and from the reported recovery of such bottles Commander Becher had drawn up his 'Bottle Chart' in 1843 (Figure 49). As cheap and easy means of measuring surface currents, drift spheres and bottles have been widely used. They can be put overboard by commercial vessels on regular runs, or in weather that makes other types of current measurement impossible. From 1885 onwards Prince Albert of Monaco, one of the founders of modern fisheries research, experimented each year with various types of drifters. The bottle illustrated (Figure 50) is of glass, so ballasted that it floats barely awash, offering minimum resistance to the wind. Cast ashore, or occasionally taken by fishermen in their nets, the bottle contained a 'break this bottle' slip, and a postcard printed in several languages which the finder was asked to fill in and return. Bottom-drifting bottles, having a drag attached, have also been used; the problem here is to make a satisfactory attachment of the drag, since if this becomes detached the bottle will thereafter act as a surface float.

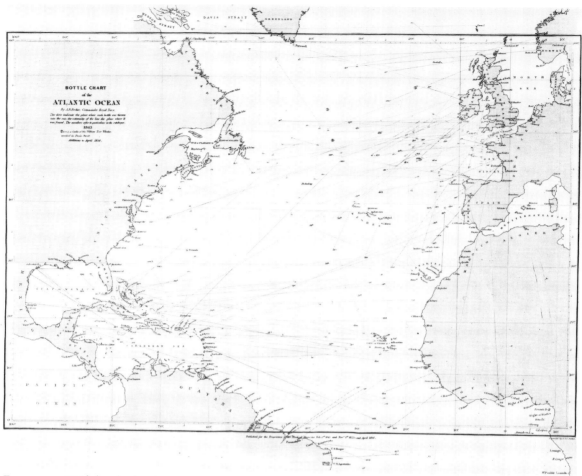

FIGURE 49 'Drift bottle chart' showing the tracks of bottles cast adrift in the North Atlantic and recovered prior to 1856

FIGURE 50 Drift bottle

Relative abundance of plankton and hence of fish may depend on quite small variations of temperature and salinity which distinguish water masses. It is vital that measurement of these parameters should be accurate and capable of fine resolution. To this end the Kristiania Laboratory devoted much attention to the construction of suitable waterbottles and thermometers.

Insulated bottles were developed at the Laboratory for use at moderate depths where heat exchange was not a problem. The older kinds of bottles had been insulated by solid walls of some badly-conducting material. This introduced the inconvenience that the bottle required some time to take up the temperature of the water level to be sampled. To avoid this, Otto Pettersson had introduced in 1894 a bottle in which insulation was effected by the sea water itself. Heat exchange between the bottle and its surroundings occurs mainly by convection within the contained water. Pettersson's bottle had walls made up of spaced concentric cylinders of thin brass or celluloid, with top and bottom lids made of rubber plates. By introducing a thermometer into the bottle after it came up these water layers tended to mix, thereby destroying the insulated effect. Nansen therefore added a modification to enable a thermometer to be secured within the bottle on its descent. This improvement, and some other technical arrangements, characterised the Pettersson-Nansen bottle, which from about 1905 became widely used in international investigations (Figure 51).

When samples are required from greater depth, the time taken to haul up a bottle becomes considerable. The likelihood of heat exchange becomes great, and the decrease in pressure as the bottle and its contents are raised results in adiabatic cooling.*

J. Richard designed a reversing bottle in 1902, for use on the *Princesse Alice*, research vessel of Prince Albert of Monaco. This bottle reversed by propeller action as it was hauled up (Figure 52). The propeller engaged a gear which released a catch, allowing the bottle to capsize and the end-valves to close on the contained water. In 1905 V. W. Ekman introduced a reversing waterbottle with a pair of reversing thermometers attached to it, all within the same frame. Ekman's bottle was messenger-operated, and this method was generally adopted for all reversing waterbottles and for thermometer frames. For work at great depths it was a saving of time to suspend several bottles at intervals along the same line. A messenger released from the ship capsized the uppermost bottle, and this in turn released another messenger to operate the next one, and so on down the line (Figure 53).

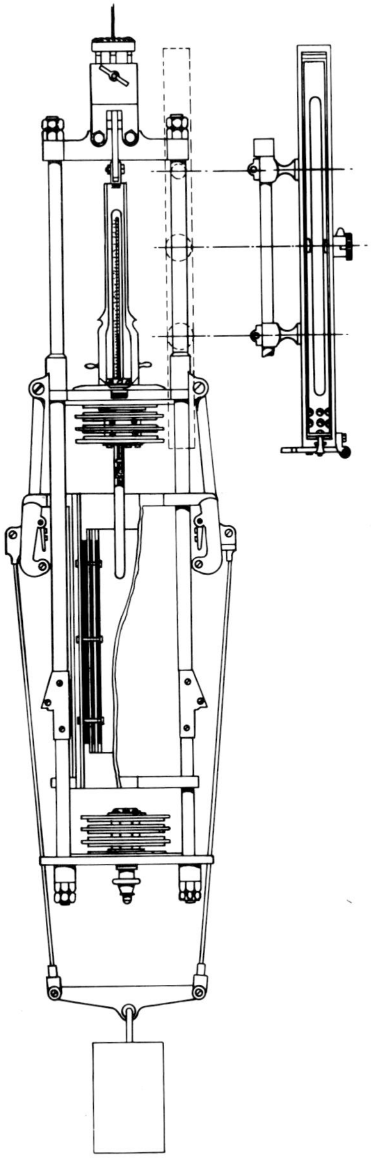

FIGURE 51 Pettersson-Nansen insulated waterbottle

* Because the insulating material of the bottle is highly compressible, and the contained water slightly so, they expand as the pressure decreases. This expansion is at the expense of internal energy, and so their temperature falls. The reverse: compression and heating, occurs on descent but can be overcome by allowing the apparatus time to take up the ambient temperature.

FIGURE 52 Richard's reversing
waterbottle

FIGURE 53 Ekman reversing
waterbottle

44

Observations of the surface water may be made merely by dipping a bucket into the sea and measuring its temperature as it is brought on to the deck. However, if there is much difference between the temperature of sea and air, or if there is a strong wind blowing, the measurement will be inaccurate. In order to obtain a more precise reading two methods have been adopted; the most simple of these being the use of an insulated thermometer. Such an instrument requires to be of sturdy construction, since it is liable to buffeting by the waves. It must adapt rapidly to the temperature of the water, and yet be slow to change once it is hauled up. The 'thermomètre plongeur', adopted by the French Navy in about 1894 was intended to resolve this apparent contradiction. The thermometer is held in a weighted brass tube, which is fitted with leather flap-valves at each end. The tube filled with water as it was lowered into the sea, and retained this as an insulant around the thermometer bulb, when it was hauled up (Figure 54).

FIGURE 54 Thermometer with insulated bulb, for taking surface temperatures

The more complex sampler developed by Lt-Cdr J. Lumby during the late 1920s was intended for use by merchant ships. It enabled them to collect samples of surface water for immediate temperature measurement and subsequent analysis, mainly for the benefit of fisheries research laboratories. The sampler was towed from the ship so that water entered the funnel, filling the bottle and surrounding the thermometer, the surplus flowing out through holes under the cap. When the sampler is hauled on board the celluloid insulating jacket keeps the enclosed water at an even temperature while the thermometer is read (Figure 55).

Plankton forms a vital part of the marine food web. Many fishes and even some whales feed on the smaller plants or animals which form part of the plankton, a term which refers to those organisms which drift more or less passively in the surrounding water.

The distribution of plankton in the sea may be so patchy that sampling at intervals with a tow-net (Figure 56) does not give a true picture. Biologists on board the research ship *Discovery* went to the Antarctic in 1925 to study the natural history of various species of whales. The daily and seasonal migrations of these animals in part follow the movements of the zooplankton on which they feed; these in turn moving vertically through the upper layers of the ocean in a diurnal rhythm, while drifting with the ocean currents. As a supplement to the tow net used at intervals it seemed desirable to construct a machine which could be towed at full speed below the surface, sampling the plankton mile by mile so as to give a continuous record of the main changes in species composition and in numbers along the line of tow. The continuous plankton recorder, developed by Sir Alister Hardy in 1925 whilst on that *Discovery* cruise, was the first of such machines (Figure 57).

As shown in the diagram, (Figure 58) the opening at the front of the recorder admits sea water into the body of the machine. A long band of fine silk gauze is arranged to wind across this flow of water, sieving out the plankton which remains pressed against it and is then sandwiched by a second band of gauze winding off a

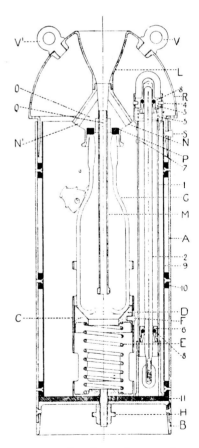

FIGURE 55 Lumby surface sampler

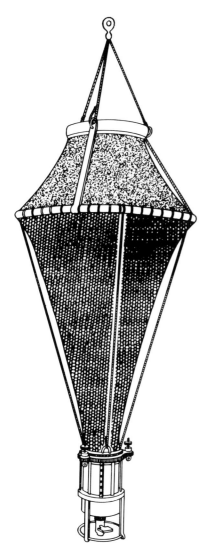

FIGURE 56 Hensen plankton net

spool soaked in formaldehyde. The two bands, together with their contained plankton, killed and preserved by the formaldehyde, are wound onto a storage spool. This mechanism is driven by the propeller at the rear, at speeds which can be altered by varying the propeller pitch. This was commonly set to wind 6 inches of gauze for each mile travelled.

By employing several recorders simultaneously from different vessels a synoptic chart of plankton distribution may be drawn, enabling its relationship with the environmental factors of water and weather to be more readily appreciated. In 1931 a regular survey was initiated, using recorders towed by commercial vessels across the North Sea. After the second world war this was extended to cover much of the North Atlantic, both merchant vessels and Ocean Weather Ships contributing to the programme.

FIGURE 57 Sir Alister Hardy with his 'Continuous Plankton Recorder' on board the *Discovery* in 1925

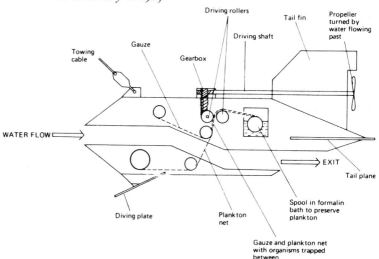

FIGURE 58 Diagram showing the interior mechanism of a continuous plankton recorder

3 MODERN OCEANOGRAPHY

Oceanographic research at the present time makes use of a wide range of continuously-recording instruments. The first of such instruments to come into regular use was the echo-sounder. In 1912 the German physicist Alexander Behm determined the speed of sound through water, but found that this varied with the density of the water and was so fast that electrical recordings of the echo tended to merge with the outgoing sound. However by 1920 he succeeded in producing a short enough signal and accurate recording equipment to take soundings in the North Sea. As a result of the recent war such information was kept secret and it seems that several governments were working along similar lines at this time. The signal used was audible, a percussion or detonation being set off at intervals. Eventually this was replaced by high-frequency sound, generated by a piezoelectric effect on a quartz crystal. The early broad-beam sounders recorded echoes from the nearest part of the sea bed which was not necessarily directly beneath the ship's keel, but the more accurate narrow-beam sounder came into use after the Second World War. The finest topographical details of the sea bed were not discovered until the narrow-beam sounder was available.

To replace the laborious analysis of recovered water samples the marine scientist may employ a single sensing unit which will telemeter back to him, or record on tape, data on the temperature, salinity, conductivity, oxygen content and sound velocity of the water in which it is placed. The same method of transmitting or recording data onto tape is used in current meters, these may be left unattended for months at a time, pre-programmed to switch on and measure the velocity and direction of the current at fixed intervals.

Since the velocity of sound through water varies with the density it is important to be able to take frequent observations of the temperature profile throughout the water column in which a vessel finds itself. The bathythermograph which was developed initially in 1938 was rapidly deployed to acquire a large amount of data, primarily for use in submarine warfare. At this period the nature of the thermocline, the layer of rapid temperature change between surface and deep water, was not well understood, and the bathythermograph was able to show the structure of this layer more readily than could be achieved by aerial measurements with water bottle and thermometer.

The bathythermograph essentially consisted of a thermal element, a xylene-filled coil; a pressure element which was a bourdon tube, and a stylus which was operated by these two elements together, so that it scribed onto a small smoked-glass plate a curve which was a graphic record of temperature against depth. This entire mechanism was contained within a weighted torpedo-shaped casing (Figure 59) and in use was allowed to fall freely through the sea, attached to a thin wire line by which it was subsequently hauled up. The smoked plate was put into a calibrated viewing holder.

The present-day bathythermograph has an expendable probe which contains sensors for detecting seawater conductivity and temperature, an electronics module and a spool of very fine wire. The probe is 'fired' from the ship, and transmits signals back along the wire to processing equipment on board so that the data is presented as a sound velocity profile. The probe is not recovered.

The ability of instruments to transmit or record data for long periods unattended means that there is no longer a need to deploy them from a ship. Such instruments may be attached to a buoyed mooring, either resting on the bottom or suspended from a surface float (Figure 60). The deep moorings contain a wire-cutting device so that at the end of a fixed period, or on command from a ship, the buoy wire is cut above the mooring weight, releasing all the instruments and the upper float. When this reaches the surface a transmitter or flashing light may be automatically switched on to aid retrieval.

The shallow-water mooring systems, which may be used with instruments to measure tidal range, or wave height, as well as current flow, are vulnerable to damage from shipping and need to be well marked by conspicuous surface buoys. Strings of instruments are also sometimes deployed from lightships.

If a water sample is required, a frameless reversing bottle is used, to which are attached pressure-protected and unprotected reversing thermometers. By comparing the readings of these two thermometers, the depth at which the bottle was reversed may be calculated directly, without the need to rely on measuring the

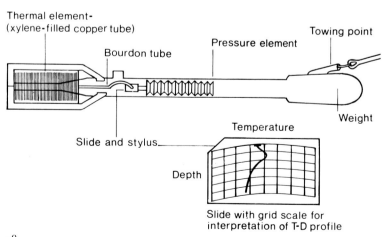

FIGURE 59 Simplified diagram of a bathythermograph

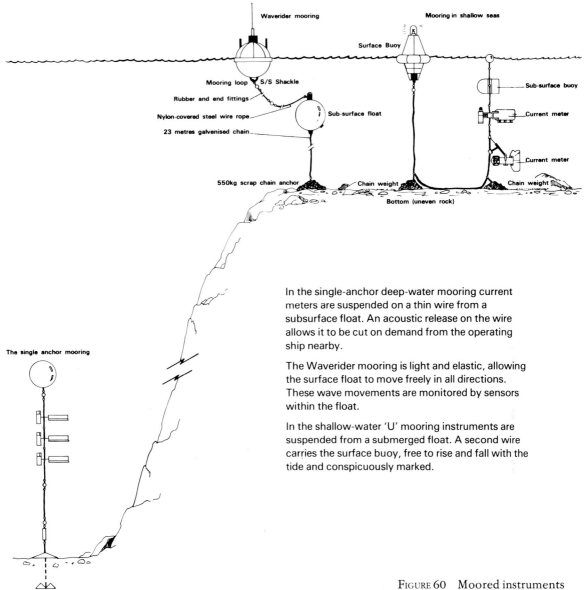

Waverider mooring

Mooring in shallow seas

Surface Buoy

Mooring loop S/S Shackle

Rubber and end fittings

Nylon-covered steel wire rope

23 metres galvenised chain

Sub-surface float

Sub-surface buoy

Current meter

Current meter

550kg scrap chain anchor

Chain weight

Chain weight

Bottom (uneven rock)

The single anchor mooring

In the single-anchor deep-water mooring current meters are suspended on a thin wire from a subsurface float. An acoustic release on the wire allows it to be cut on demand from the operating ship nearby.

The Waverider mooring is light and elastic, allowing the surface float to move freely in all directions. These wave movements are monitored by sensors within the float.

In the shallow-water 'U' mooring instruments are suspended from a submerged float. A second wire carries the surface buoy, free to rise and fall with the tide and conspicuously marked.

FIGURE 60   Moored instruments

length of wire paid out. Sea bed samples may be taken, according to the type of sample needed, by grabs, dredges or corers, and on occasion material is collected by underwater craft provided with suitable equipment.

One rapidly-developing method of collecting oceanographic data is that of putting sensors into satellites orbiting the globe. It is possible to monitor surface temperature, surface roughness and some biological phenomena by this means, while photography can yield further information.

The tendency today is to set up various long-term programmes, with international cooperation, aimed at resolving certain problems. These are often inter-disciplinary; oceanographers and meteorologists study the atmosphere and oceans and the links between these two. Oceanographers and geologists are studying the sea floor around the margins of the tectonic plates which make up the mobile crust of the globe. With the cooperation of engineers the oceanographers are also investigating the possibility of underwater extraction of economic minerals, the construction of drilling rigs and the building of other large offshore structures. Fisheries research continues, and schemes for the farming of various fish and shellfish species are under way in many parts of the world.

Seven-tenths of our globe is covered by water, but as demographic and economic pressures increase on the land areas, we shall inevitably turn more and more to the oceans in the hope that they will provide additional food and raw materials for the world's population. We need to increase our knowledge of the oceans and the part that they play in the global cycles of the atmosphere and of the solid earth.

Further reading

P. C. Badgley, L. Miloy, L. Childs: *Oceans from space.*
  Houston. Gulf Publishing Co, 1969

H. Barnes: *Oceanography and marine biology, a book of techniques.*
  London. George Allen and Unwin, 1959

G. E. R. Deacon: *Oceans, an atlas-history of man's exploration of the deep.*
  London. Paul Hamlyn, 1962.

M. Deacon: *Scientists and the Sea, 1650–1900.*
  London. Academic Press, 1971.

W. Herdman: *Founders of oceanography.*
  London. Edward Arnold, 1923.

E. Linklater: *The voyage of the Challenger.*
  London. John Murray, 1972, and Cardinal, 1974.

J. Murray and J. Hjørt: *The depths of the ocean.*
  London. Macmillan, 1912.

S. Schlee: *A history of oceanography, the edge of an unfamiliar world.*
  London. Robert Hale. 1975.

Scientific American: *Oceanography, readings from Scientific American 1952 to 1971.*
  San Francisco. W. H. Freeman, 1971.

V. Ponko: *Ships, seas and scientists. US Naval exploration and discovery in the nineteenth century.*
  Annapolis. Naval Institute Press, 1974.

A. E. J. Went: *Seventy years agrowing, a history of the International Council for the Exploration of the Sea, 1902–1972.*
  Copenhagen. Rapports et Procès-verbaux des réunions ICES 1972.

C. Wyville-Thomson: *The depths of the sea. An account of the general results of the cruises of HMSS Porcupine and Lightning during the summers of 1868, 1869 and 1870.*
  London. Macmillan, 1873

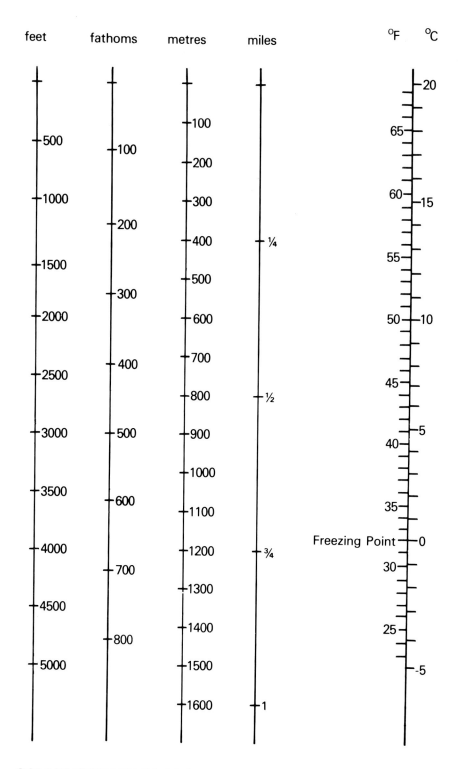

feet	fathoms	metres	miles	°F	°C
					20
				65	
500	100	100			
		200			
1000	200	300		60	15
		400	¼		
1500		500		55	
	300	600			
2000		700		50	10
2500	400	800	½	45	
3000	500	900		40	5
		1000			
3500	600	1100		35	
4000		1200	¾	Freezing Point	0
	700	1300		30	
4500		1400		25	
	800				
5000		1500			-5
		1600	1		

CONVERSION TABLE FOR DEPTHS AND TEMPERATURES.
Source: British Standard 350 pt 2. 1962.

Shelf seas are less than 180m; mean ocean depths are 6000m; the greatest depth known at present is 13,000m.

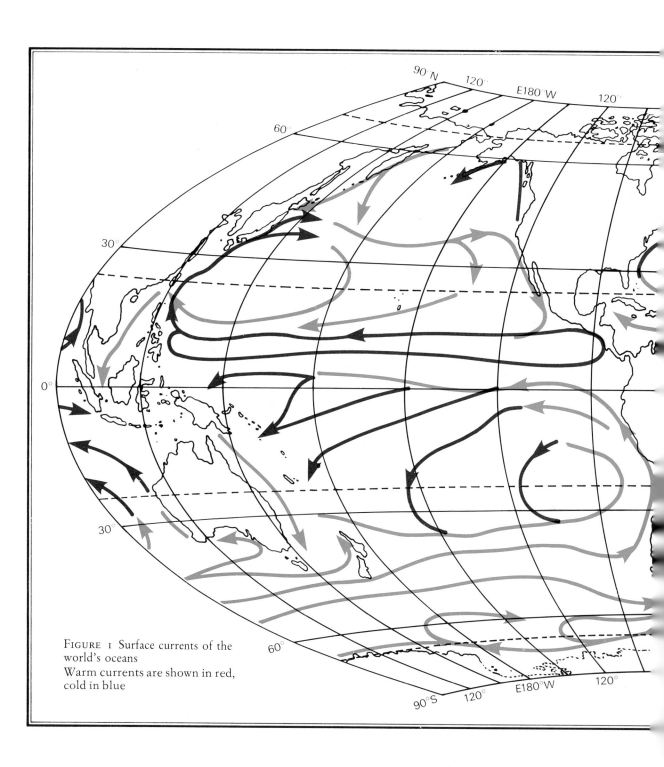

FIGURE 1 Surface currents of the
world's oceans
Warm currents are shown in red,
cold in blue